PRINTING

AND THE

ALLIED TRADES

By

R. RANDOLPH KARCH

Technical Supervisor
Department of Publishing and Printing
Rochester Athenaeum and Mechanics Institute
Rochester, New York

Introduction by
JOHN CLYDE OSWALD

Revised and Enlarged Edition

LONDON
SIR ISAAC PITMAN & SONS, LTD.
1939

SIR ISAAC PITMAN & SONS, Ltd.
PITMAN HOUSE, PARKER STREET, KINGSWAY, LONDON, W.C.2
THE PITMAN PRESS, BATH
PITMAN HOUSE, LITTLE COLLINS STREET, MELBOURNE

ASSOCIATED COMPANIES
PITMAN PUBLISHING CORPORATION
2 WEST 45TH STREET, NEW YORK
205 WEST MONROE STREET, CHICAGO

SIR ISAAC PITMAN & SONS (CANADA), Ltd.
(INCORPORATING THE COMMERCIAL TEXT BOOK COMPANY)
PITMAN HOUSE, 381–383 CHURCH STREET, TORONTO

PREFACE

An attempt has been made in the revision of this book to give a four-fold service—to provide a text to serve:

1. As a junior and senior high school text and work-book in industrial arts printing courses.

2. As a related subjects text and shop work-book for the beginning years of vocational high school and trade school printing courses.

3. As a reference- and hand-book for printing apprentices.

4. As a handbook on printing processes for journalists, advertising people and others who have contact with printers.

These functions depend upon how the book is used.

The sections on type, spacing material, straight composition, proving and correcting, distribution and presswork may serve as a junior high school informatory manual. The problems and project sections, keyed to the text, will serve as a self-assigning work-book.

The sections on display composition, in addition to the junior high school section, and in the more advanced brackets, may serve as a senior high or trade school informatory manual and work-book.

The chapters on the allied trades, in addition to the above, will give information important to the related subjects class, held either in the shop itself or in the classroom.

Apprentices, journalists and advertising people will find the informatory pages invaluable, as well as such sections as samples of type faces, display composition, printing plates, and accident and health hazards.

Supplementary readings are listed at the end of each chapter. This makes additional information easy to find in the event that a deeper study into a subject is desired.

Following each chapter is a list of questions for class discussion. Numbers of informatory paragraphs are placed after each question to facilitate study.

Objective tests, comprehensive in content, make possible a guide for self-testing or for periodic examination in all areas. The writer suggests that small cards be printed, with rows of numbers, a place for a name, grade and date, to give to each student who takes these tests. A key having correct answers can then be made, thus facilitating marking.

Jobs in the problem and project section are keyed to the text by section numbers for easy reference by the student.

The author acknowledges his indebtedness to the following for kindly advice and for material used in illustrating this book: Mr. John H. Chambers, Education Department, International Typographical Union; Mr. John Backus, Education Department, American Type Founders Sales Corporation; the late Miss Honora Jacob, Norwood High School, Norwood, Ohio; Mr. John J. Metz, Editor, *Industrial Arts and Vocational Education*; Baltimore-Maryland Engraving Company; S. D. Warren Company; Indianapolis Engraving Company; Challenge Machinery Company; Goss Printing Press Company; Chandler & Price Company; Modern Die & Plate Manufacturing Company; Wood, Nathan & Virkus Company; Hammermill Paper Company; Mergenthaler Linotype Company; Intertype Corporation, Ludlow Typograph Company; Lanston Monotype Machine Company; *Liberty Magazine*; Stokes & Smith Company; Thompson-National Press Company; Harris-Seybold-Potter Company,

American Photo-Engravers Association, The Printing Machinery Company, and the following Rochester, New York,
firms: Culver-Herald Engraving Company, Rochester Electrotype & Engraving Co., the R. M. Myers Paper Company,
and Alling and Cory Company.

R. RANDOLPH KARCH

ROCHESTER, NEW YORK
March, 1938

CONTENTS

INTRODUCTION

PRINTING is to my mind the most important and interesting industry in the world. It is important because our whole educational system is based upon it. As people learn to use their minds and as their learning increases, culture is enhanced.

Printing is the handmaid of business. Without printing business as now conducted would cease to function. Printing is largely responsible for increase of wealth. A machine or process is invented in a given locality and a new branch of industry is thereby created. The facts about it are put into print and distributed in other localities, and the knowledge thus made available is converted into action; other enterprises are brought into being wherever the facts become known.

Printing is an art. Practically all the principles employed in the fine arts—form, proportion, color, tone, balance, harmony, contrast,—apply to the printed page just as to painting or any other form of art.

Printing is interesting because of its traditions. Born at a time when the world was emerging from the long centuries of the so-called Dark Ages, the first printed books have an interest not to be found in the product of any other industry.

Therefore, the young man or woman who decides to follow a career connected in some way with printing is to be congratulated. Someone has said,"Blessed is he who finds joy in his work." There is work which, it must be acknowledged, is drudgery, but printing does not come within that classification.

The goal which most young persons at the start of their careers have in mind is eventually to secure a competence and independence. There is "no royal road" to fortune. Most owners of printing establishments began their careers at the case or press. Success means mastery of principles, careful attention to details, thoroughness in completion of the task in hand. This method, applied as one goes through the years step by step, means almost certain arrival at the goal.

Mr. Karch has set forth in the pages of this book in a clear, concise, and well illustrated manner the fundamentals of printing practice. This volume will help the student to master them and he will find himself on the right road. Thorough understanding of what is here presented will make the next steps easy. The author, printers, and publishers are to be congratulated for this splendid text.

JOHN CLYDE OSWALD

CHAPTER I

A BRIEF HISTORY OF PRINTING

1. *The First Movable Type*—It has been proved beyond reasonable doubt that the Chinese printed from movable type as early as the eleventh century. However, as the Chinese alphabet consisted of several thousand characters this method of printing was impractical in that country, and consequently did not find favor.

2. *Wood Block Printing*—Printing from wooden blocks was practiced long before movable type was in use. The characters or illustrations were cut in relief on a smooth board, and ink was dabbed on the surface. The paper was placed over the block, and then rubbed down to take the impression.

The earliest dated print is the "Saint Christopher," struck off in 1423. This was probably not the first block print, but it is the first one of which we have extant proof.

Soon "Block Books" appeared, which consisted of several prints bound together. The subjects were invariably that of saints and images.

3. *Johann Gutenberg*—Prior to the invention and practice of printing from movable types, all books were made in "scriptoriums," where they were laboriously copied by hand. For this reason, books were very rare, and consequently very expensive. The fertile brain of Johann Gutenberg, of Mainz, Germany, conceived the idea of assembling letters and spaces to form a page, and pulling many impressions from this type form. The type form could then be broken up, and the letters used again to print succeeding pages of the work. Gutenberg's first type style was copied from the bold, angular writing of the scribes.

Existing records show that Gutenberg was experimenting with movable type as early as 1439. Johann Fust, a goldsmith, and Peter Schoeffer, his clerk, were associated with Gutenberg until they set up their own establishment.

4. *The First Books Printed from Movable Type*—As far as is known, the first work of Gutenberg was the 31-line Indulgence of November 12, 1454, issued by Pope Nicholas V. This document granted privileges to those who assisted in financing the campaign of the King of Cyprus against the Turks.

The Mainz Psalter, printed by Fust and Schoeffer in 1457, was the earliest book to contain the name of the printer and the date of publication.

5. *The Bibles*—The earliest printers soon turned their creative art to the production of Bibles. The most famous of these is the "42-line" or "Mazarin" Bible, which was printed at Mainz. It is not known definitely whether Gutenberg or Fust and Schoeffer executed this masterpiece. The former, however, is usually given credit for this work.

A second Bible is known as the "36-line Pfister," or "Bamberg" Bible. This edition was issued about 1460, and, like the 42-line Bible, was printed at Mainz. The type and style identifies this work to be that of Gutenberg.

The third edition of the Latin Bible is the finest production of the three. This was the first Bible to carry the date, and was printed in two volumes by Fust and Schoeffer.

6. *The Spread of Printing*—From the invention of printing to the end of the fifteenth century, the art of printing found its way through all parts of Germany. At the beginning of the sixteenth century, presses had been established in no less than fifty towns, and over 200 printers were at work.

7. *Printing in Italy*—In 1465, two German printers, Conrad Sweynheym and Arnold Pannartz, established their press at the Benedictine monastery of St. Scholastica, where they issued the first book printed in Italy, a "Donatus pro puerulis." No copy of this work has survived.

The bold, angular type face of the German printers was not popular in Italy. Nicholas Jenson, a Frenchman, was the first to produce books printed in the pure roman-faced type, which found instant popularity with the Italians. Jenson established himself at Venice, where, from 1470 to 1480, he produced over 150 editions.

In 1501 Aldus Manutius introduced the italic type, which was designed from a model of Petrarch's handwriting. "The Virgil" was the first book printed in the new italic type. This marked the beginning of a series of small editions printed especially for the poorer patrons.

8. *Printing in France*—In the year 1470, two professors of the Paris Sorbonne invited three German printers, Gering, Kranz, and Freiburger, to set up a press in the university. Here was issued the first book printed in France, "The Epistolae Gasparini," in 1470.

9. *Printing in England*—In 1477, William Caxton printed the first book in England, "The Dictes and Sayengis of the Philosophers." Caxton printed over 100 books after this time. Many of Caxton's type faces are used today in modernized form.

10. *Printing in America*—It is believed that the first press to be set up in America was established in Mexico in the year 1536. The study of printing in Mexico has brought out the fact that 118 volumes were printed in Mexico up to the year 1600.

In 1638, Rev. Jose Glover succeeded in importing a printing press to British North America. Stephen Daye, who was influenced to come to America with the press by Rev. Glover, set up the equipment in Harvard College, at Cambridge, Massachusetts. The first printing, done in 1639, was entitled "The Freeman's Oath." The first book to be produced by the press was "Psalms in Meter," which was struck off in 1640.

The first regular American newspaper, "The Boston Newsletter," was printed from 1704 to 1776. This forerunner of our great American dailies was printed in the shop of Bartholomew Green.

QUESTIONS FOR CLASS DISCUSSION

1. Explain why printing from movable type was not practical in China.   1.

2. When was the first dated block print made?   2.

3. What is a "scriptorium"?   3.

4. When and where, and by whom, was printing invented?   3.

5. What advantage is there in printing books from movable type over the ancient method?   3.

6. Name several of the first books printed from movable type, and their makers.   4, 5.

7. How did roman type originate? Italic?   7.

8. When was printing introduced in this continent?   10.

9. When and where was the first press established in British North America?   10.

BOOKS FOR FURTHER READING

HAYNES, "The Student's History of Printing," McGraw–Hill Book Co.

OSWALD, "A History of Printing," D. Appleton & Co.
OSWALD, "Benjamin Franklin, Printer," Doubleday, Page & Co.
U. T. A. TYPOGRAPHIC LIBRARY, Vols. 49 to 54, inclusive.
MCMURTRIE, "The Book," Covici-Friede.
OSWALD, "Printing in the Americas," Gregg Publishing Co.

CHAPTER II

MODERN PRINTING

11. *Commercial Printing*—Although mainly interested in the production of books, the early printers from time to time issued single informatory sheets, chapbooks, and catalogs of a crude sort.

Printing was a very expensive process up to the introduction of mechanical devices, such as the power press, stereotyping, photography, electrotyping, mechanical paper making, and finally the typesetting machine. By 1840 the practice of printing was brought to the point where it was economically possible to produce subjects other than books.

12. *Printing an Important Industry*—One out of every 283 working people in the United States is employed in some form of publishing and printing. There are almost 32,500 printing establishments, large and small, scattered throughout the country. In fact, almost every small village has its print shop.

Recent government statistics bring to light that printing, listed with 273 other manufacturing industries, ranks first in the number of establishments and in added value by manufacturing, second in wages, fourth in value of products, sixth in wage earners, and thirteenth in cost of material.

13. *Printing Specialists*—Today printing is a highly specialized craft, divided into three main divisions:

1. Printing from raised surfaces, known as "letterpress printing."

2. Printing from plane surfaces, known as "lithography."

3. Printing from depressions in a plate, known as "intaglio" printing.

The importance of the printing industry as a whole is

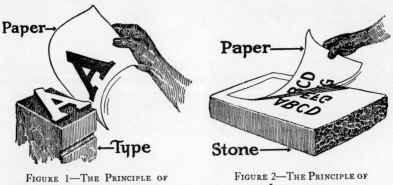

FIGURE 1—THE PRINCIPLE OF
LETTERPRESS PRINTING.

FIGURE 2—THE PRINCIPLE OF
LITHOGRAPHY.

dependent mostly upon the letterpress method. Each class of letterpress printing is a highly specialized art: newspaper and

FIGURE 3—THE PRINCIPLE OF INTAGLIO PRINTING.

magazine printing, book printing, and general commercial printing. However, the work in each may be classified as follows:

1. Composition, where the types are set, corrected, made up into forms and locked up into chases for the press,

2. Pressroom, where the type forms are placed on the presses, and paper is printed.

3. Bindery, where the paper stock is cut to size, and other work, such as folding, trimming, stitching, sewing, and tabbing is done.

13a. *The "silk screen process,"* a stencilling device, is used for short runs on advertising display. The work can be done on all types of rough or smooth materials with great facility. Both opaque and transparent colors are used.

Silk, organdie, or metal screening is stretched tightly over a frame, which is hinged to a work table. To make a "hand-cut" stencil, the design is cut from a thin, tough paper, and glued to the under side of the screen. The material to be printed is laid under the screen, and a squeegee is used to force the pigment through the screen not covered by the stencil. A photographic method is also used in making the screen.

QUESTIONS FOR CLASS DISCUSSION

1. What inventions are responsible for the growth of printing?   11.

2. Discuss the importance of printing.   12.

3. What are the three methods of printing?   13.

4. What method is the most important?   13.

5. Name the three departments of a print shop, and tell what processes are carried on in each.   13.

6. Explain "silk screen printing."   13a.

BOOKS FOR FURTHER READING

I. T. U. Typographic Library, Vol. 29.

Clark, "The Printing Trades and Their Workers," International Textbook Co.

CHAPTER III

FOUNDRY TYPE

14. A *Type* is a strip of metal about an inch high, having a letter standing out in relief on one end. Each type is wonderfully accurate in its shape and proportions, no matter how small it is made.

15. *Type Height*—The exact height of all American type is .918 ($\frac{918}{1000}$) of an inch. Type heights differ in foreign countries. In England the height is .917; France, Germany and Spain, .928; and Bulgaria, .936.

16. *Type Metal*—Type is composed of an alloy of lead, tin and antimony. Tin acts as a binder and toughens the metal, while antimony gives it hardness. Copper is often added in small quantities. This composition shrinks very little in cooling in the mold when cast, and leaves a smooth, closely grained surface that is very durable.

17. *Parts of a Type*—Figure 4 illustrates a type with its parts labeled. The "face" is the part that makes the impression on the paper. "Serifs" are the short cross-lines at the ends of the main strokes. The "counter" is the hollow part within and around the face. The "shoulder" is the top of the type below the face. The "beard" is the beveled space below the face. The "pin mark" is made by the pin which removes the type from the mold after casting. Very often the pin mark bears the trade mark of the type founder, or the size of the type. "Nicks" act as guides to the typesetter, and ofttimes differentiate between type faces of the same size. The "feet" are the two projections on which the type

9

stands. The "groove" is formed by the tool that removes the jet after the type is cast.

A "kern" is that part of the face that extends over the side of the body. Kerns are usually found on the letters f and j.

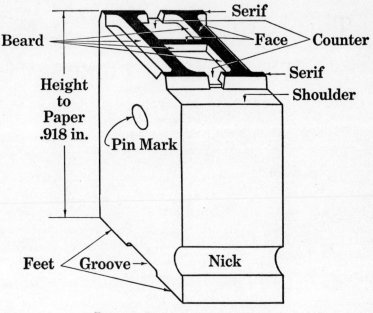

FIGURE 4—PARTS OF A PRINTING TYPE.

18. *Type Fonts*—A "font" of type is an assortment of any one size and style. A font includes "caps" (capital letters), "lower case" (small letters), figures, and "points" (punctuation marks). Often SMALL CAPITALS, reference marks (asterisk *, dagger †, double dagger ‡, section §, parallel ‖, paragraph ¶), fractions, diphthongs (Æ, Œ, æ, œ), special characters (ct, st), and "ligatures" (fi, ff, fl, ffi, ffl). The use of ligatures prevents the kerned letter f from breaking when set against tall letters.

19. *Kinds of Type*—Types may be classified into five main divisions: roman, gothic, italic, text and script.[1] Each of these five classes may be divided again into bold face, condensed, extended, outline, shaded, and so on. Figure 5 illustrates these basic type designs.

This is Roman Body Type

This is Bold Face

This is Italic

This is Text

This is Script

This is Shaded

This is Gothic

This is Outline

This is Condensed

This is Extended

SWASH INITIAL LETTERS

FIGURE 5—BASIC DESIGNS OF TYPE.

[1] The American gothic is known as "sans serif" in Europe. The European gothic is America's black-face text.

20. *"Modern" and "Old Style"*—Roman faces are either "old style" or "modern." Modern type has greater regularity of shape, more accurate curves, and delicate serifs and hairlines. Old style is noted for its diagonally sloping serifs. Further, old style is adapted to rough finished paper, while modern shows to advantage on hard finished paper. See Figure 6.

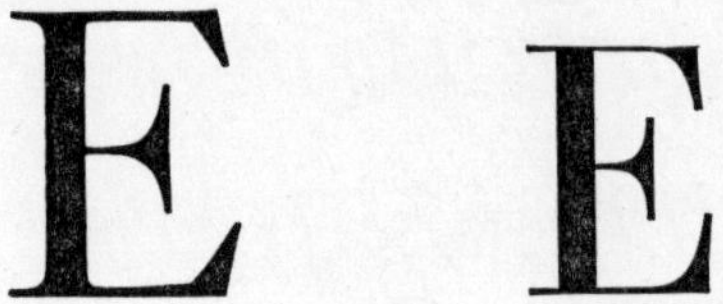

FIGURE 6—OLD STYLE.   MODERN.

21. *Type Families*—Members of a "type family" have the same general appearance, except that some faces may be either light, bold, italic, extended or condensed, as the case may be. The Caslon Family is illustrated in Figure 7.

22. *The Point System*—Because of the very small sizes of type, a system of measurement is used called the "point system." The "point" is the unit of measure, and is about $\frac{1}{72}$ of an inch (to be exact, it is .0138 inch.) A "nonpareil" (pronounced non-per-el') is equal to 6 points. The "pica" (pronounced pī'-ca) equals 12 points. There are 6 picas in one inch. It behooves the printing student to have these measurements fixed in his mind, as all printing measurements are made in this manner.

23. *The Em*—The pica is usually termed the "em," based on the 12-point em. Thus 12 ems is 12 picas, 23 picas is 23 ems, and so on.

24. *The Pica Rule*—The printer's ruler is known as a "pica rule" or "line gauge." Inches are usually stamped on

Caslon Antique

Caslon Antique Italic

Caslon Oldstyle

Caslon Oldstyle Italic

Caslon Openface

Caslon Clearface

Caslon Clearface Italic

Caslon Medium

Caslon Medium Italic

Caslon Black

Caslon Black Italic

Caslon Black Condensed

Caslon Catalog

FIGURE 7—THE CASLON FAMILY OF TYPE FACES.

one side, and picas and nonpareils on the other. Figure 8 shows the use of the pica rule.

25. *Sizes of Type*—Before the introduction of the point system of type measurement in 1878, sizes were known by names: 5 point was called "Pearl," "Brevier" was 8 point, for example. The new system of measurement was obviously a great improvement.

By the term "48-point type" is meant that the type is 48 points, or 4 picas thick, measuring the face the shoulder, as shown in Figure 8.

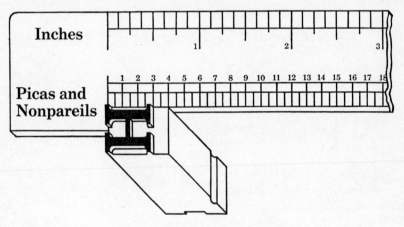

FIGURE 8—THE USE OF THE PICA RULE.

26. *Type Series*—Typefounders make type in a graded series from 6 point to 72 point. The usual sizes are 6, 8, 10, 12, 14, 18, and thence in multiples of 6 points to 60 point. Occasionally, sizes as small as 3 point are made, and as large as 144 point. A series of type from 6 to 72 point is shown in Figure 9.

27. *Wood Type*—Large wood type, such as is used in printing signs and posters, is so made to decrease the weight and the cost. These large faces are usually measured by the pica-line. Thus 6-line type is 6 picas thick, and 15-line type is 15 picas thick.

6 point—Gutenberg, the father of the printing art, established his first press in the city of Maintz, Ge

8 point—Gutenberg, the father of the printing art, established his first press in the city o

10 point—Gutenberg, the father of the printing art, established his fir

12 point—Gutenberg, the father of the printing art, established

14 point—Gutenberg, the father of the printing art, est

18 point—Gutenberg, the father of the prin

24 point—Gutenberg, the father of

30 point—Gutenberg, the

36 point—Gutenberg, t

42 point—Gutenber

48 point—Gutenb

60 point—Gu

72 Point-G

FIGURE 9—A SERIES OF "EUSEBIUS" TYPE.

28. *Storage of Type*—Each font of type is kept in its own "case," consisting of a shallow drawer divided into many

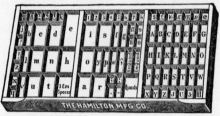

FIGURE 10—A CALIFORNIA JOB CASE.

small compartments. In each compartment is kept certain groups of letters. Figure 10 illustrates the "California Job Case," which is the most popular style. A "pair of news

FIGURE 11—A PAIR OF NEWS CASES.

cases" consists of an upper and a lower case, shown in Figure 11. The upper case contains caps and often small caps, while the lower case contains the lower-case letters. There are very many styles of type cases, in fact, too many

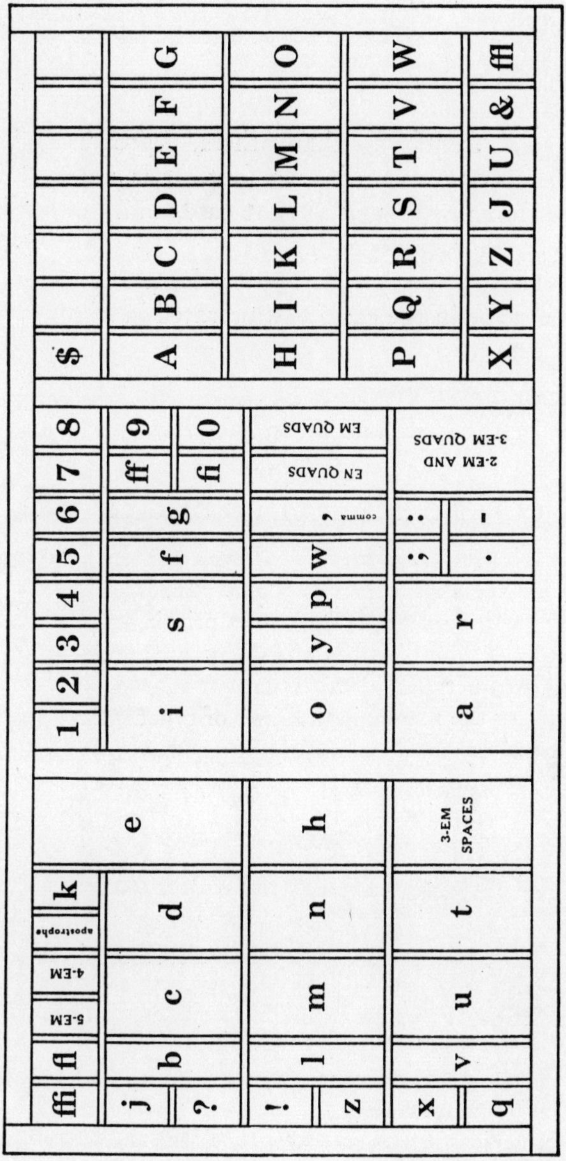

FIGURE 12—THE LAYOUT OF A CALIFORNIA JOB CASE.

to endeavor to explain in this book. Type cases are kept in "cabinets" and "case racks."

29. *The Case Layout*—As some letters of the alphabet are used more frequently than others, a greater supply of these types are provided in the font. It is necessary that these types have more space in the case, and for this reason the boxes are of varying sizes.

It is necessary for the printing student to learn the location of each type in the case, as illustrated in Figure 12.

30. *Learning the Case*—An excellent method used to learn the arrangement of the letters in the case is to make a diagram of the case, and fill in the characters until memorized.

QUESTIONS FOR CLASS DISCUSSION

1. Why is it necessary for types to have a uniform height? 14, 15.
2. Of what metals is type composed? 16.
3. Name and describe the parts of a printing type. 17.
4. What is a "font" of type? Why are ligatures provided with some fonts of type? 18.
5. What are the five main divisions of type? 19.
6. Differentiate between old style and modern type. 20.
7. Give two reasons for placing nicks on type. 17.
8. Explain the point system. 22.
9. What is a type series? What is a type family? 26, 21.
10. Make a drawing of a California Job Case and indicate the location of each letter and character. 28, 29, 30.

BOOKS FOR FURTHER READING

DE VINNE, "Plain Printing Types," Oswald Publishing Co.

FRAZIER, "Type Lore," Inland Printer Co.

UPDIKE, "Printing Types: Their History, Forms and Uses," Harvard University Press.

U. T. A. TYPOGRAPHIC LIBRARY, Vols. 1, 2, 3, 4 and 16.

CHAPTER IV

SPACING MATERIAL

31. *Leads and Slugs*—Leads and slugs are thin strips of metal, used to separate lines of type. They are made to even pica and nonpareil sizes, and are stored in specially designed cases. In Figure 13 is pictured one of the many styles of lead and slug racks.

Leads are either 1, 2, or 3 points in thickness, the most popular size being 2-point. The term "set solid" is applied

FIGURE 13—ONE STYLE OF LEAD AND SLUG RACK.

to all type matter set without leads or slugs between the lines. The relative sizes of leads and slugs are given in Figure 14. Leads and slugs are purchased in long strips, to be cut to size by the printer, or in "labor-saving fonts" that are ready cut to lengths from 4 to 25 picas.

32. *Piecing Leads*—It is often necessary, when setting type, to combine leads and slugs when there is not a sufficient quantity of the required length to finish the work.

When this is done, the joint should not come at the same place in each line, as this would cause the type form to break

---

Thickness of a 1-Pt. Lead

Thickness of a 2-Pt. Lead

Thickness of a 6-Pt. Slug

Thickness of a 12-Pt. Slug

FIGURE 14—RELATIVE SIZES OF LEADS
AND SLUGS.

at this point in handling. Figure 15 illustrates the proper manner of piecing leads.

FIGURE 15—PROPER MANNER OF PIECING
LEADS AND SLUGS.

33. *Spaces and Quads*—Spaces and quads are used to blank out between words, at the ends of paragraphs and to form indentions. The thinnest blanks up to one-third of an em are called "spaces"; those one-half em and larger are called "quads." Spaces and quads are usually cast without nicks—a guide is not needed because spaces and quads may be turned in any position.

34. *The Em Quad* is the square of the type body of any size of type, and is the unit by which all other spaces and quads are measured. An eight-point em quad measures 8×8 points; a 14-point em quad measures 14×14 points, and so on.

The 3-em space is one-third the width of the em quad, and is the standard space used between words in setting type. The 4-em space is one-quarter of an em quad, and the 5-em space is one-fifth of an em quad. In the new "Point-Set System" the spaces vary slightly from these proportions, as shown in Figure 16. A hair space is usually 1 point in

Body Size	3-em Space	4-em Space	5-em Space	Thin Space
6-point.......	2 pts.	$1\frac{1}{2}$ pts.	$1\frac{1}{4}$ pts.	1 pt.
8-point.......	3 pts.	2 pts.	$1\frac{1}{2}$ pts.	$1\frac{1}{4}$ pts.
10-point.......	$3\frac{1}{2}$ pts.	$2\frac{1}{2}$ pts.	2 pts.	$1\frac{3}{4}$ pts.
12-point.......	4 pts.	3 pts.	$2\frac{1}{2}$ pts.	$1\frac{3}{4}$ pts.
14-point.......	5 pts.	4 pts.	3 pts.	2 pts.

FIGURE 16—STANDARD WIDTHS OF POINT-SET SPACES.

thickness, and a sufficient number of types are furnished with fonts above 12 point. One-half point and 1-point copper and brass spaces, respectively, are obtainable in all type sizes. These are invariably kept in a special case provided.

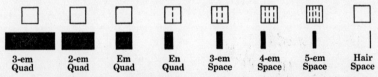

| 3-em Quad | 2-em Quad | Em Quad | En Quad | 3-em Space | 4-em Space | 5-em Space | Hair Space |

FIGURE 17—RELATIVE SIZES OF SPACES AND QUADS.

The 2-em quad is twice the thickness of the em quad, and the 3-em quad is three times the size of the em unit. This size facilitates blanking out large white spaces at the ends of lines. Type fonts 30-point and larger usually have no 2- and 3-em quads. Figure 17 shows the relative sizes of spaces and quads used in composing type.

35. *Reglet* are strips of wood similar to slugs, only longer, and are used in large poster work and in locking up type

 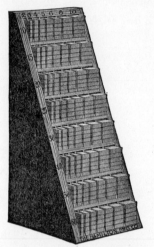

FIGURE 18—REGLET RACK.

FIGURE 19—A CASE OF WOOD FURNITURE.

forms for the press. Reglet may be bought in labor-saving sizes, however.

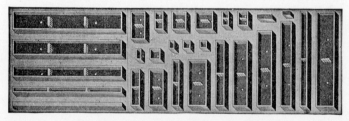

FIGURE 20—A FONT OF METAL FURNITURE.

36. *Furniture*—This spacing material is used to fill out large blank spaces. Wood furniture, used for locking up type forms for the press, is cut in labor-saving sizes. Metal furniture is used to fill out blank spaces within the type form, where accuracy is paramount. Wood and metal furniture are both made up in sizes for use: widths of 2, 3, 4, 5, 6, 8 and 10 ems, metal lengths of 4, 5, 6, 8, 10, 15, 20 and 25 ems, and wood lengths of 10, 15, 20, 25, 30, 35, 40, 50 and 60 ems. The material may be purchased in much larger sizes to be suitable for certain classes of work.

37. *Cup Cast Quads* are similar to the regular quads, usually with a hollow center. They are very useful in setting blank form work. Labor-saving fonts from 2×4 to 2×20 picas are made.

37a. *Non-Distribution System*—In large shops, where the "non-distribution system" is used, spacing materials of all kinds are cast in long strips on machines, cut to size when needed, and after printing the jobs are thrown into the metal pot with the type matter, which is used only once.

QUESTIONS FOR CLASS DISCUSSION

1. Explain the use of leads and slugs.   31.
2. How should leads be pieced?   32.
3. What is meant by "solid matter"?   31.
4. What is the "em quad"?   34.
5. Name the spaces. What relation has each to the em quad? 33, 34.
6. Name the quads. What relation has each to the em quad? 33, 34.
7. What is the purpose of metal furniture? Wood furniture?   36.
8. What are the uses of reglet?   35.
9. For what class of work are "cup cast quads" useful?   37.
10. What is meant by "labor-saving material"?   31.
11. What is the "non-distribution system"?   37a.

BOOKS FOR FURTHER READING

U. T. A. TYPOGRAPHIC LIBRARY, Vol. 2.

CHAPTER V

STRAIGHT COMPOSITION

38. *Plain Composition* in ordinary paragraph form is known as "straight composition," or "body matter." Body types are usually a plain roman type face. This text is set in body type known as 11-point New Caslon on 13-point body.

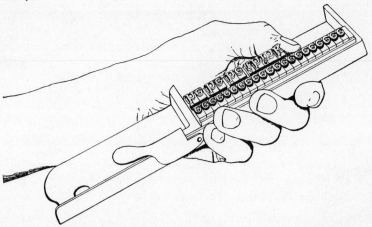

FIGURE 21—A COMPOSING STICK HELD IN THE CORRECT MANNER.

39. The *Composing Stick*—The printer sets type in a "composing stick," which is a small receptacle usually made of steel, adjustable to various widths of lines. Figure 21 illustrates the stick, held in the proper manner in the left hand, with the thumb holding the last line being composed.

40. *Setting the Stick*—To keep leads and slugs from bind-ing, the stick must be set slightly wider than the wanted width. The "graduated stick" is so set to even multiples of 6-point ems. If the stick is not graduated, the setting should be to the required measure of 12-point quads, plus a thin sheet of paper, or a copper $\frac{1}{2}$-point space.

41. *Justification*—Making each line of type the same width is called "justification." A properly justified line will stand by itself in the stick with no support other than its own tightness. A line should never be set so tightly, how-

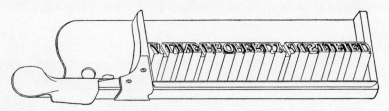

FIGURE 22—A LINE PROPERLY JUSTIFIED.

ever, that it is difficult to remove a type from the assembled line. Figure 22 shows a line properly justified, so that it stands by itself in the stick.

42. *Spacing*—In spacing a line, the 3-em space is set first between words. However, this space may be either too large, or too small to bring the line to the required length. A detailed explanation of how lines are spaced follows:

43. *Decreasing Space between Words*—If a small amount of space is needed to get the last word or part thereof in the line, the following procedure is carried out:

1. Substitute as many 4-em spaces for the 3-em spaces as are necessary to gain the required space.

2. If the 4-em spaces are too large, substitute as many 5-em spaces for the 4-em spaces in as many places as are necessary to gain the required space.

3. If absolutely necessary, the hair space may be set between words after a comma, and between types that have open spaces on the side of the face; as between a word ending in w and a word beginning with j.

44. *Increasing Space between Words*—In the event that the last word almost fills the line, and there is not sufficient space left to accommodate the next word, it is necessary to substitute *thicker* spaces for the 3-em space first put in. The following procedure is carried out:

1. Substitute en quads for the 3-em spaces in as many places as is necessary to tighten the line. Except at the ends of paragraphs, under no circumstances are spaces placed at the end of a line.

2. If the line is still loose after en quads have been substituted for the 3-em spaces, substitute a 3-em space and a 4-em space combined in as many places as is necessary to tighten the line.

3. If the combination of 3-em and 4-em spaces does not tighten the line, substitute two 3-em spaces combined in as many places as is necessary to tighten the line.

4. If the combination of two 3-em spaces combined does not make the line tight, substitute a 3-em space and an en quad combined in as many places as will tighten the line.

Some words appear to have more space between them than others, even when identical spaces are used. For example, the space between a word ending in y and a word beginning with v appears to have more space than is between such letters as l and h. Therefore, when substituting thinner or thicker spaces in justifying a line, this fact is considered by the compositor, and spacing is done accordingly.

Figure 23 illustrates the method of substituting thicker and thinner spaces in order to space and justify a line of straight matter.

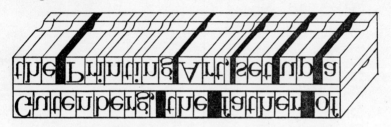

Gutenberg, the father of the Printing Art, set up a

FIGURE 23—THE SUBSTITUTION OF SPACES AND QUADS IN JUSTIFYING A LINE.

45. *Space between Sentences* is often made slightly larger than that between words in the same line. Spaces larger than the em quad of the type should not be used, however.

46. *Dividing Words*—Often the last word in a line must be divided to avoid awkward spacing. Words are divided according to pronunciation—according to syllables. The dictionary should be freely used to determine the correct division of words. More than two divisions in successive lines should be avoided, and no divisions should be made unless absolutely necessary.

47. *Quadding Out*—When spacing out at the ends of paragraphs, spaces and quads should be arranged so that the largest quads are placed at the end of the line. If the arrangement is reversed, and small spaces are placed at the ends of

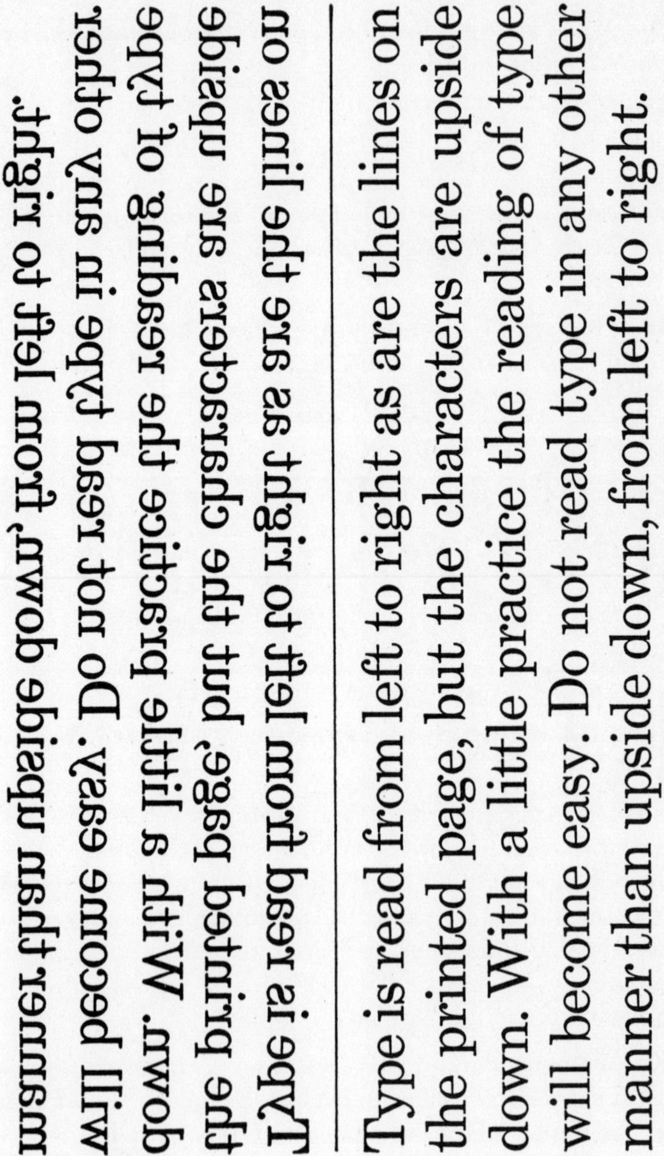

Type is read from left to right as are the lines on the printed page, but the characters are upside down. With a little practice the reading of type will become easy. Do not read type in any other manner than upside down, from left to right.

Type is read from left to right as are the lines on the printed page, but the characters are upside down. With a little practice the reading of type will become easy. Do not read type in any other manner than upside down, from left to right.

FIGURE 24—READING TYPE.

the line, they are very likely to cause trouble when the type is removed from the stick.

48. *Reading Type Matter*—As a line of type is set from the left of the stick to the right, the reading thereof should be done likewise. Type is set in reverse, so that the reading will necessarily be from the bottom of the form up the stick. Figure 24 shows the type form at the top, and the printed form below.

49. *Puzzling Letters*—The type characters d, b, q, and p appear very similar to the beginner, and usually cause him

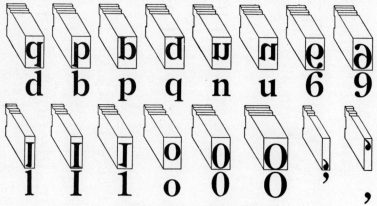

FIGURE 25—PUZZLING LETTERS.

much trouble unless he learns to distinguish one from the other at the outset. Likewise, the n and u, the 6 and 9, the 1, I and l, the o, 0 and O, and the comma (,) and apostrophe (') are puzzlers. The chart given in Figure 25 will be helpful to the novice in learning these characters.

50. *Centering a Line*—By setting the same number of identical spaces and quads on each side of a line, it is known to be "centered." Headings are invariably centered.

51. *Setting Points*—The following rules in spacing points (punctuation marks) are invaluable to the beginner:

1. No space is set before the comma and the period.

2. No space is set on either side of the apostrophe when it is contained in a word, or on either side of the hyphen when it is contained in a compound word.

3. A 1-point space is usually set before the colon (:), semicolon (;), exclamation mark (!), and interrogation mark (?). Set a 1-point space on either side of the em dash (—).

52. *Setting Quotation Marks*—First quotation marks are formed by turning two commas nick down ("). The last quotation marks are made by setting two apostrophes together ("). No space is set between the marks and the quoted sentence.

53. *Setting Caps*—Because of the thickness of the letters, caps look better if en quads are used for spacing. Caps should be set in as wide a measure as possible to facilitate spacing.

54. *Paragraph Indentions*—Paragraphs are usually indented to be of assistance to the reader. Type matter 18 ems wide and under should be indented 1 em quad; from 19 to 25 ems, $1\frac{1}{2}$ ems; and from 26 ems up, 2 ems of the type body. If possible, the last line of the paragraph should not be full.

55.

Hanging Indention—This style of indention is useful in newspaper and magazine advertisements. The first line is set full, and each succeeding line is indented from 1 to 2 ems, depending upon the width of the matter set. This paragraph is set in the hanging indention style.

56.

The Half-Diamond Indention is used on various classes of
work, such as advertisements, motto cards, etc. The
first line is set to full measure, and the second
is indented from 1 to 2 ems on each side.
The third is indented in like proportion,
and so on. Each line must be centered. This paragraph is set in
the half-diamond style.

57.

Diagonal Indention—The diagonal style of indention is often used on programs and kindred work.
The first line is set flush with the left side of the
stick, and each succeeding line is indented 1 em
more than the line above it.   This paragraph is
set in the diagonal indention style.

58.

Squared Indention—The squared indention brings
prominence to certain important informatory text.
Caps or bold face is generally used, being squared
and centered in the measure, as is this paragraph.

59. *Indenting Poetry*—In poetry, lines that rhyme should
be set with equal indention. If two lines together rhyme,
there is usually no indention made. Some lines of poetry
overrun the measure, and these are taken care of by indenting them one em more than the most heavily indented lines.
Quotation marks should extend into the margin, if possible,
so they will not disturb the vertical alignment of the cap

letters. Figure 26 illustrates the points given in this paragraph.

> "Royal and Dower-royal, I the Queen
>   Fronting thy richest sea with richer
>   hands—
> A thousand mills roar through me where
>   I glean
> All races from all lands."

FIGURE 26—POETRY INDENTION.

60. *Letterspacing*—Letterspacing is resorted to only when it improves the appearance of the type form. In some cases, it is better to letterspace than have unusually large spaces between words. Copper $\frac{1}{2}$-point spaces are best for this work. No space should be set between words which, because of their shape, seem to be farther apart than others. Letterspacing especially improves a line of large cap letters. For example, in the word AWAIT, which should be letterspaced only on each side of the cap I, thus: AWAIT.

61. *Leaders* are types upon which are cast either dots or hyphens, aligned with the bottom of the type face, placed at intervals in open lines to guide the eye across to figures or other words, as in indexes, tables of contents, etc. Leaders are cast by typefounders in sizes from 5 point to 18 point, in several styles. Durable brass leaders are procurable for certain classes of work. Leaders are cast in en (.), em (..), 2-em (....) and -em (......) sizes with one, two or three dots to an em. Usually, leaders have two dots to an em, as in this text. The use of leaders is shown in Figure 27.

In leader work, figures should line on the right column. The largest number should be used as a basis, and shorter numbers lined underneath. To justify the lines, spaces must not be set between leaders; only between the leaders and the words. An en quad is usually set between the leaders and the figures.

Old Name	Point Size	Ems to Foot
Pearl..................	5..................	173
Nonpareil..............	6..................	166
Minion................	7..................	125
Brevier................	8..................	108
Bourgeois.............	9..................	96
Long Primer...........	10.................	86
Small Pica.............	11.................	79
Pica..................	12.................	72

FIGURE 27—THE USE OF LEADERS.

62. *Multiple Justification*—When setting short measures, as in tables of several columns of figures, justification is made against a slug which just fills all subsequent columns. This is accomplished by setting the first column against the longest rule; the rule is removed, and a shorter one set into place.

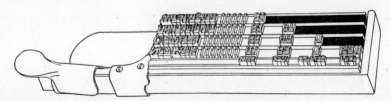

FIGURE 28—HOW TO SET THE STICK FOR SETTING SHORT MEASURES.

Then the next column is justified. Figure 28 illustrates the procedure in setting tables with multiple justification.

63. *Roman Numerals*—The Roman numeral is made up of regular capital or small capital letters. On most work, the period is omitted, although it is found in a great many cases.

Roman figures are aligned on the right side, a result achieved by setting the longest quantity first, and later indenting the others to align with it, shown in Figure 29.

```
  I A Brief History of Printing
 II Modern Printing
III Type
 IV Spacing Material
  V Straight Composition
```

FIGURE 29—HOW TO SET ROMAN NUMERALS.

64. *Ditto Marks* relieve the printer from the task of re-setting the same words many times in the same column. The ditto mark is made by turning two commas nick down. The marks must be centered under each word, as shown in Figure 30.

```
Three 2-point leads equal  6 points
Four   "   "      "    "   8   "
Five   "   "      "    "   10  "
Six    "   "      "    "   12  "
```

FIGURE 30—THE USE OF DITTO MARKS.

65.

INITIAL LETTERS—The plain initial letter, as shown here, is an invaluable aid in guiding the eye to the starting point of a paragraph in reading, and adds a decorative effect to the work. In this paragraph, note how the margins surrounding the initial are equal. The first word or phrase is set either in caps or small caps.

THE same principle is involved in keeping identical margins when using the initial T, as illustrated in this paragraph. Note that all lines are the same length following the initial letter. The same style is followed with the letters W and Y.

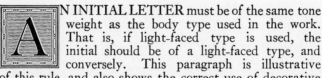N INITIAL LETTER must be of the same tone weight as the body type used in the work. That is, if light-faced type is used, the initial should be of a light-faced type, and conversely. This paragraph is illustrative of this rule, and also shows the correct use of decorative initial types.

ACCEPTING the above principles, the letter A and other letters of like shape must be mortised to allow the first line of type to come sufficiently close. This paragraph is an example of the use of the mortised initial. The cutting was carefully done on a power saw trimmer.

QUESTIONS FOR CLASS DISCUSSION

1. What is meant by "straight composition"? 38.
2. Why should the stick be set slightly wider than the measure wanted? 40.
3. What is meant by "justification"? 41.
4. What space is used first between words in setting type? 42.
5. Discuss the procedure of decreasing space between words. 43.
6. Discuss the procedure of increasing space between words. 44.
7. How about space between sentences? 45.
8. What rule can you give for quadding out lines? 47.
9. Distinguish between the q, p, d, and b. 49.
10. Distinguish between the n and u, 6 and 9. 49.
11. Distinguish between the 1, I and l. 49.
12. How are quotation marks set? 52.
13. What can you say about the setting of caps? 53.
14. What indentions are made in paragraphs, according to widths? 54.
15. Explain the following: hanging indention, half-diamond indention, diagonal indention, squared indention. 55, 56, 57, 58.
16. Discuss the indenting of poetry. 59.
17. When is letterspacing advisable? 60.

18. What can you say about the use of leaders?   61.
19. What is meant by "multiple justification"?   62.
20. Discuss the alignment of roman numerals. Ditto marks.   63, 64.
21. Discuss the use of initial letters.   65.

BOOKS FOR FURTHER READING

CHICAGO UNIVERSITY PRESS, "Manual of Style."
DE VINNE, "Correct Composition."   The Century Co.
U. T. A. TYPOGRAPHICAL LIBRARY, Vols. 16 and 20.

CHAPTER VI

PROVING AND CORRECTING

66. *Removing Type from the Stick*—After a stickful of type is set, it is removed and placed in a flat tray, called a

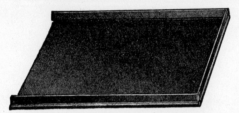

FIGURE 31—ONE STYLE OF GALLEY.

galley (Figure 31). The method shown in Figure 32 will assist the beginner in performing this operation. If the type is

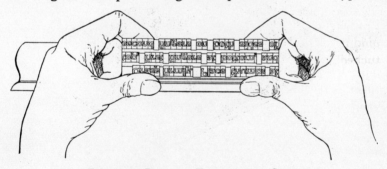

FIGURE 32—REMOVING TYPE FROM THE STICK.

grasped firmly, it will not be reduced to "pi" (mixed or spilled type). Type is always placed in a galley with the nicks to the open end.

67. *Tying Up Type*—One end of a string of sufficient length is held in the left hand, while the right draws the

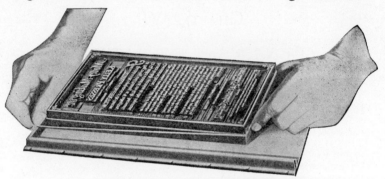

FIGURE 33—WRAPPING THE STRING AROUND THE TYPE FORM.

string around the form, starting at the upper left-hand corner. Each layer of string should lap over that preceding in order to

FIGURE 34—FASTENING THE STRING IN TYING UP A TYPE FORM.

bind it. This leaves only one end of the string loose, which is tucked in with a lead between the layers of string, as shown in Figures 33 and 34. No knot is tied. The end of the string should protrude in order to draw out the string readily in untying the form.

68. *Pulling a Proof.*—After the type form is tied securely so that each unit is held upright, the galley is placed on the "proof press." (Figure 35 pictures one form of proof press.) With the ink "brayer," or roller, the type is sufficiently inked. Then a sheet of paper is laid over the form, and the press operated so that the cylinder will press the paper

FIGURE 35—ONE STYLE OF PROOF PRESS.

FIGURE 36—AN INK BRAYER.

against the type. After proving, the form should be thoroughly cleaned with gasoline or benzine.

69. *Hand Proofs*—Large jobs that can not be proved on the press must be done by hand. The form is inked in the usual manner, and a dampened sheet of paper carefully laid over it. A felt-covered "proof planer" (a wooden block) is placed lightly on the sheet and tapped gently with a mallet.

70. *Proofreading*—Before type matter may go to press, it is necessary carefully to scan the proof to see that no errors appear. Errors are noted by certain standard marks, and this copy is used in correcting the type matter.

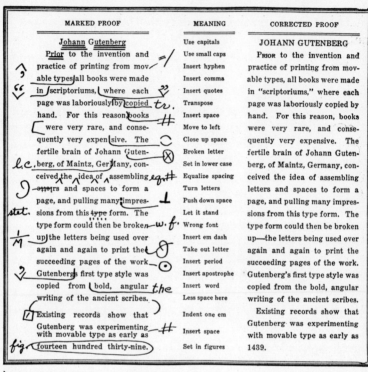

MARKED PROOF	MEANING	CORRECTED PROOF
Johann Gutenberg	Use capitals	JOHANN GUTENBERG
Prior to the invention and	Use small caps	Prior to the invention and
practice of printing from mov	Insert hyphen	practice of printing from mov-
able types all books were made	Insert comma	able types, all books were made
in scriptoriums, where each	Insert quotes	in "scriptoriums," where each
page was laboriously by copied	Transpose	page was laboriously copied by
hand. For this reason books	Insert space	hand. For this reason, books
were very rare, and conse-	Move to left	were very rare, and conse-
quently very expen sive. The	Close up space	quently very expensive. The
fertile brain of Johann Guten-	Broken letter	fertile brain of Johann Guten-
berg, of Maintz, Germany, con-	Set in lower case	berg, of Maintz, Germany, con-
ceived the idea of assembling	Equalize spacing	ceived the idea of assembling
and spaces to form a	Turn letters	letters and spaces to form a
page, and pulling many impres-	Push down space	page, and pulling many impres-
sions from this type form. The	Let it stand	sions from this type form. The
type form could then be broken	Wrong font	type form could then be broken
up the letters being used over	Insert em dash	up—the letters being used over
again and again to print the	Take out letter	again and again to print the
succeeding pages of the work	Insert period	succeeding pages of the work.
Gutenberg first type style was	Insert apostrophe	Gutenberg's first type style was
copied from bold, angular	Insert word	copied from the bold, angular
writing of the ancient scribes.	Less space here	writing of the ancient scribes.
Existing records show that	Indent one em	Existing records show that
Gutenberg was experimenting	Insert space	Gutenberg was experimenting
with movable type as early as		with movable type as early as
fourteen hundred thirty-nine.	Set in figures	1439.

X	Defective letter	⊙	Colon	no ¶	No paragraph
⊥	Push down space	;	Semicolon	w.f.	Wrong font letter
ᘒ	Turn over	∨	Apostrophe	stet	Let it stand
⊖	Take out	∨	Quotation	tr.	Transpose
∧	Insert at this point	-/	Hyphen	Caps	Capitals
✓	Space evenly	///	Straighten lines	S.C.	Small capitals
※	Insert space	⊏	Move over	l.c.	Lower-case letter
⌣	Less space	☐	Em quad space	ital.	Italic
⌒	Close up entirely	|—1	One-em dash	Rom.	Roman letter
⊙	Period	|—2	Two-em dash	(?)	Verify
⁄	Comma	℔	Make paragraph	O	Spell out

FIGURE 37—STANDARD PROOFREADERS' MARKS.

71. *Proofreaders and Copyholders*—The "proofreader" is usually graduated to this position from that of a journeyman. The "copyholder" assists the reader by holding the original copy and reading slowly and distinctly, observing all punctuation. The reader not only marks the literal errors, but preserves the office grammatical style, corrects spacing, and other mistakes. The reader can not make alteration from the original copy—if author's copy is obviously wrong, the error should be "queried" in the margin of the proof and sent for examination.

72. *Marking Errors*—In Figure 37 a list of proofreaders' marks is shown, which marks are practically standard in all printing establishments. Errors should be marked in the margin—if marked between the lines of the text, they may be overlooked by the printer. To avoid misunderstanding, the period and colon are enclosed in circles. The hyphen is followed by a diagonal stroke, and an inverted caret is usually placed over the comma.

73. *Making Corrections*—After proving and reading, the galley of type is placed on an inclined surface so that the type will stand upright, and untied. Few corrections can be made without taking the type from the stick, owing to the irregular widths of the letters. It is easier to correct each line in the stick than to attempt to change the spacing of a line in a galley. Lines are removed from the form as shown in Figure 38. The line is firmly gripped on all sides to keep it from being "pied."

74. *Overrunning Type*—Very often, in correcting, when a word or more has been left out, it is necessary to "overrun" a word or syllable to the next line, and continue until the "out" has been included. The best way to handle this is to place the lines in order forming one long line on a galley, pick up in order and respace in the stick.

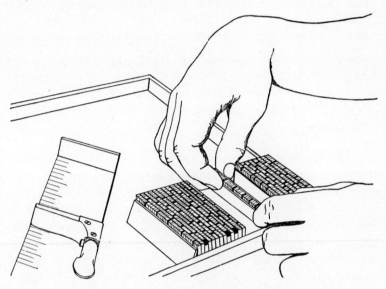

FIGURE 38—PICKING UP A LINE TO REPLACE IN THE STICK FOR CORRECTION.

75. *A Revise* is a proof taken after corrections have been made, to check on corrections.

QUESTIONS FOR CLASS DISCUSSION

1. What is printer's "pi"?   66.
2. Explain the method of tying a type form.   67.
3. How are proofs pulled on a proof press?   68.
4. How are proofs pulled by hand?   69.
5. What are the duties of a proofreader? A copyholder?   70, 71, 72.
6. How should corrections be made in a line of type?   73.
7. How is type overrun?   74.
8. What is a "revise"?   75.

BOOKS FOR FURTHER READING

DE VINNE, "Correct Composition," The Century Co., New York.

I. T. U. TYPOGRAPHIC LIBRARY, Vols. 5, 17, 32 to 41, inclusive.

SMITH, "Proofreading and Punctuation."

TEALL, "The Compounding of English Words," The Inland Printer Co.

UNIVERSITY OF CHICAGO PRESS, "Manual of Style."

U. T. A. TYPOGRAPHICAL LIBRARY, "Proofreading."

Chapter VII

DISTRIBUTION

76. The term "distribution" embraces the placing of type and spacing materials back into the cases and racks after use. Type ready for distribution is called "dead" matter. "Live" matter is yet to be printed.

77. *Distributing Straight Matter*—When distributing type, the beginner should pick up only two or three lines at the start. As skill develops, he can take larger amounts without fear of spilling.

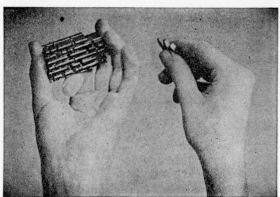

FIGURE 39—HOLDING TYPE FOR DISTRIBUTION.

78. *Holding Type for Distribution*—Type is taken from the galley in the same manner as in lifting lines for corrections. The type is then shifted to the left hand, nick up, and balanced as shown in Figure 39.

Beginning with the right end of the top line, a whole word is taken between the index finger and the thumb as shown. Each word should be read before distributing. If this is done, there will be no doubt as to the identity of each puzzling letter. Type set in too long a measure to be handled safely must be placed in a stick for distribution.

If the form contains more than one size and style of type, the different fonts should be first sorted, each kind being placed in a galley alone. Then each galley is carried to the cabinet wherein the respective fonts are stored.

78a. *Non-Distribution System*—The "breaking-up" and throwing into a truck for remelting of machine composed type and spacing material comes under the heading of distribution. Type and material can be set so cheaply by machine that it can be used only once.

79. *Mixing Fonts*—To prevent the mixing of type fonts, two or more characters from the case should be compared with the dead matter before distribution. Nicks must be compared, and faces closely checked to keep the cases clean.

80. *Distributing Leads and Slugs*—If there is more than one size of leads and slugs in the dead form, they are stood on a galley, and arranged in order with reference to the different sizes. Do not pick material from a pile.

QUESTIONS FOR CLASS DISCUSSION

1. What is the term used for type ready to be distributed? 76.
2. What term is used for type forms to be printed? 76.
3. How should type be held for distribution? 78.
4. How are various sizes and styles of type handled in distributing? 77, 78.
5. What rules can you give for keeping the type cases clean? 79.
6. Explain an easy way to distribute leads and slugs. 80.
7. What is meant by "non-distribution"? 78.

Chapter VIII

BORDER AND RULE

81. *Borders* are characters cast in units or strips, in many designs, which may be adjusted in many sizes and shapes, as for marginal lines, panels, and other decorative uses.

82. *Foundry Borders*—Type-cast foundry borders are made in 3, 6, 12, 18, 24, 30 and 36-point sizes, in a multitude

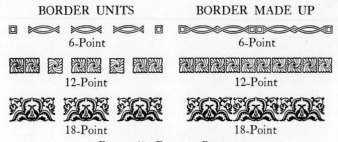

FIGURE 40—FOUNDRY BORDERS.

of designs. A font of foundry border usually contains pieces of various lengths, which may be assembled to enclosed forms of any shape or size. A few examples of foundry borders are shown in Figure 40, which are stored in special cases.

83. *Machine Borders*—Linotype borders are cast in 30- or 42-pica strips, and point sizes of 6, 12, 18, 24 and 36 point. The monotype casts both unit borders, as foundry type, and line borders in strips of any desired lengths from 2-point to

24-point sizes. The Elrod casts strip material in line borders, similar to the monotype.

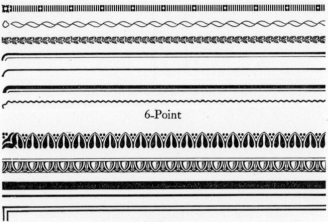

6-Point

12-Point

FIGURE 41—MACHINE BORDERS.

Strip borders must be cut to size on a "slug-cutter" or "saw trimmer." Corners are mitered on a 45° angle either on a hand miterer or a "rotary miterer," the latter doing the work in the twinkling of an eye.

BORDER UNITS   BORDER MADE UP

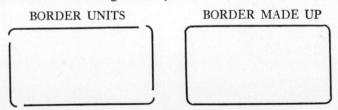

FIGURE 42—FORMING PANEL BORDER WITH MACHINE BORDER.

84. *Rules*—Rules are used in composition where plain lines are required. Rules are made in many thicknesses and styles of face.

85. *Brass Rule*—Being more durable than machine rule, brass rule is the most popular in certain classes of work.

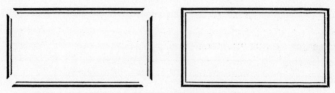

FIGURE 43—MACHINE RULE MITERED TO FORM A PANEL.

Brass rule has both top and bottom prepared as a printing surface, and is obtainable in labor-saving fonts, cut in pieces from 1 to 36 picas, with 6-point sizes from $1\frac{1}{2}$ to $9\frac{1}{2}$ picas.

Showing Each Printing Face of 6-Point Column Rule

Showing Each Printing Face of 2-Point Beveled Rule

Showing Each Printing Face of 2-Point Center Face Rule

FIGURE 44—THREE STYLES OF BRASS RULE, SHOWING PRINTING
SURFACES OF BOTH SIDES.

These fonts of rule are kept in special cases, as shown in Figure 46.

Brass rule may be obtained in many thicknesses, from 1 point to 24-point, and many styles of face. The most-used styles, however, are those shown in Figure 44: 2-point rule with $\frac{1}{4}$-point center face, 2-point rule with $\frac{1}{4}$-point beveled face, and 6-point column rule, used by newspapers. Each style has two printing surfaces, as shown.

Beveled rule is made so that a well-fitting abutment can be made, as shown in Figure 45.

86. *Machine rule* is available in strips from 2- to 18-point thicknesses on the monotype and Elrod. The linotype casts

<table>
<tr><td></td><td></td><td></td></tr>
</table>

Center Face Rule—Poor Abutment

<table>
<tr><td></td><td></td><td></td></tr>
</table>

Beveled Rule—Good Abutment

FIGURE 45—FITTING CENTER FACE AND BEVEL RULE.

hairline faces to full 6-point faces on a 6-point type body, in lengths of 30 or 42 picas.

FIGURE 46—A BRASS RULE CASE.

87. *Setting a Border*—It is customary for the compositor to assemble his border and marginal spacing before setting the type for the job in hand. This made-up border is called the "skeleton" of the form. No slugs are needed outside the border other than at the head and the foot. In making up the marginal space, slugs are set full length of the form—and the slugs for the widths are set inside the side slugs.

88. *Lining Type with Rule*—When using rule with type, it is necessary to set the rule in perfect alignment with the bottom of the type face. The face of the rule and the face of the type must also be in harmony, i.e., light-face type should

Name_____
(Rule properly aligned)

Name_____
(Inharmonious)

Name_____
(Improper alignment)

Name _____
(Harmonious)

FIGURE 47—LINING BRASS RULE WITH TYPE.

be used with light-faced border; heavy type with heavy border. This rule is exemplified in Figure 47.

QUESTIONS FOR CLASS DISCUSSION

1. What two styles of border are in use? 82, 83.
2. What is meant by "strip material"? 81, 83.
3. What advantages has brass rule over machine rule?   85.
4. What style of rule is used to get a good abutment?   85.
5. What rule should be kept in mind when setting rule with type? 88.
6. What is the best way to miter a border? 83.

Chapter IX

SETTING DISPLAY COMPOSITION

89. *Display*—In all kinds of composition certain important lines of type are "displayed," or strengthened to attract the reader's eye. This makes selectivity in reading quick and easy.

90. *Methods of Display*—A line of type may be displayed in three ways:

1. By a contrast in sizes and shapes of type faces.
2. By isolating a line or word, and
3. By printing in a different color.

For example, if a line of 12-point type is set in a job of 8-point type, the larger line is displayed, being more prominent by reason of the contrast in size. The greater the contrast the more we find a line displayed.

91. *Minor Display*—Display words of minor importance are emphasized in the following ways: By setting in CAPS, SMALL CAPS, *italics*, **bold face**, or by underscoring.

92. *Displaying the Right Element*—The subject of the job in question should at all times be displayed. The word "Look," as displayed in Figure 48, may attract general attention, but the word "Suits" directs attention to the advertised product. A better display is shown in Figure 49, which delivers the message quickly and easily, and makes the "pulling power" of the advertisement greater.

93. *Over-Display*—Contrast is the keynote of display. In Figure 50 the important lines do not stand out sufficiently. This is caused by a lack of contrast between the important lines and the balance of the type matter. As reset in Figure 51, an improvement is made by setting the important lines in larger type, and the rest in smaller type.

FIGURE 48—DISPLAYING THE WRONG ELEMENT.

FIGURE 49—RIGHT ELEMENT DISPLAYED.

94. *Forms of Display*—The most popular form of display is that of the balanced long and short lines, as shown in Figure 50. The half-diamond indention follows next, and the squared form of display, shown in Figure 52, is often used when the nature of the copy makes this possible.

HARMONY

95. *Harmony*, as applied to printing, means a state of a pleasing relation between the parts of a piece of printed matter.

96. *Harmony of Type Faces*—To secure a pleasing typographic effect, it is preferable to use members of the same

LINCOLN
THE INSPIRING
STORY OF HIS LIFE
TOLD BY
GEORGE W. HENDRICKS
MUSIC HALL
WEDNESDAY EVENING
MARCH 26

FIGURE 50—OVERDISPLAY.

LINCOLN
THE INSPIRING
STORY OF HIS LIFE
TOLD BY
GEO. W. HENDRICKS
Music Hall
Wednesday Evening
March 26

FIGURE 51—CORRECT DISPLAY.

BEFORE SAILING
IN THE SUMMER
Deposit your securities with us and we will collect income due and remit draft.
HOME SAVING &
LOAN COMPANY

FIGURE 52—THE SQUARED FORM OF DISPLAY.

type family. Figure 53 shows very poor form in using several families of type in the same set-up, which is very inharmonious. In Figure 54 a much more pleasing effect is obtained by the use of one family of type.

GOTHIC

𝔐𝔦𝔵𝔢𝔡 𝔴𝔦𝔱𝔥

BOLD FACE

and Italic Faces

Not Good Form

Where The Use of

ONE SERIES

Is Used, We

Find Good

Form

FIGURE 53—AN INHARMONIOUS SELECTION OF TYPE FACES.

FIGURE 54—AN HARMONIOUS SELECTION OF TYPE FACES.

Caslon
Black

**Face Type
Alarms**

Medium
Caslon

Of a Lighter
Weight

Clearface
Caslon

Type Face
Charms

FIGURE 55—BLACK ELEMENTS IN HARMONY.

FIGURE 56—MEDIUM ELEMENTS IN HARMONY.

FIGURE 57—LIGHT ELEMENTS IN HARMONY.

Old style and modern type faces, being so unlike in form, should never be used in the same piece of composition. Old

English (black-face text) and block gothic may be used if the latter is much subdued—the gothic about one-half to three-quarters as tall as the lowercase Old English letters.

97. *Harmony of Tone*—Type faces, border and ornament, contained in the same set-up, should be of the same degree of density to secure tone harmony. A black border used with light type is bad form; likewise light border with black type is inharmonious. Figures 55, 56, and 57 illustrate the harmony which is obtained by using type, ornament and border of the same degree of density.

98. *Shape Harmony*—A harmony in shape exists when the parts of the work are similar in shape. A long, narrow

Thin
Faces
in Good
Form
Here

WIDE FACES

LOOK WELL IN

WIDE SPACES LIKE THIS

FIGURE 58—SHAPE HARMONY BETWEEN TYPE AND PANEL.

FIGURE 59—SHAPE HARMONY BETWEEN TYPE AND PANEL.

job is harmonious if set in a long, narrow face, as shown in Figure 58. In a wide job, as shown in Figure 59, a wide or extended face lends harmony of shape.

BALANCE AND PROPORTION

When the parts of a piece of type composition are equalized and pleasing, it is said to be "balanced."

99. *Optical Center*—In balancing a job, the "optical center" must be considered, rather than the exact, or "mathematical" center. To the normal eye the exact center of a rectangle appears slightly lower than it actually is. This is

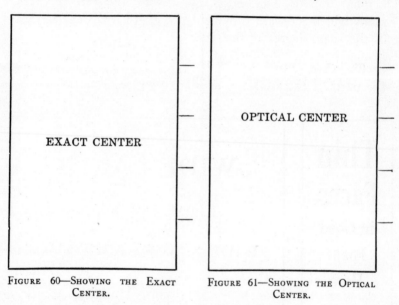

FIGURE 60—SHOWING THE EXACT CENTER.   FIGURE 61—SHOWING THE OPTICAL CENTER.

readily seen by examining Figures 60 and 61, which illustrate the exact and optical centers of a rectangle. The optical center is approximately two-fifths below the top of the rectangle.

100. *Balance*—When one group of type matter is placed out of center, it is necessary to balance it with another group which is diametrically opposite. Balance is determined by the rule, "the smaller is to the larger as the larger is to the whole." This rule is illustrated in Figures 62 and 63. Note the lack of balance in Figure 62, and the well-balanced groups of type in Figure 63. The groups of type are of unequal weight

THE

REBAL ENGINE

A Newly
Published Catalog
Describing Our New Model
Gasoline Engine for
Manufacturing
Purposes

❧

BROWNLY CORPORATION
Cincinnati, O.

FIGURE 62—A LACK OF BALANCE.

THE

REBAL ENGINE

A Newly
Published Catalog
Describing Our New Model
Gasoline Engine for
Manufacturing
Purposes

❧

BROWNLY CORPORATION
Cincinnati, O.

FIGURE 63—A WELL-BALANCED PAGE.

—therefore the last two lines, or the lighter group, are placed farther away from the center. In this placing of unequal groups, the distance from the center line will be inversely proportional to their weight. Thus the smaller group is half the size of the larger, the center of that group will be twice the distance to the center of the larger group.

101. *Proportion* concerns the comparative relationships between the various parts of the type composition. The proportion of 2 to 3 is the generally accepted ratio for page margins. This means that the margins between the type and the border should be smaller than the margin between the border and the edge of the sheet. Figure 64 illustrates an in-

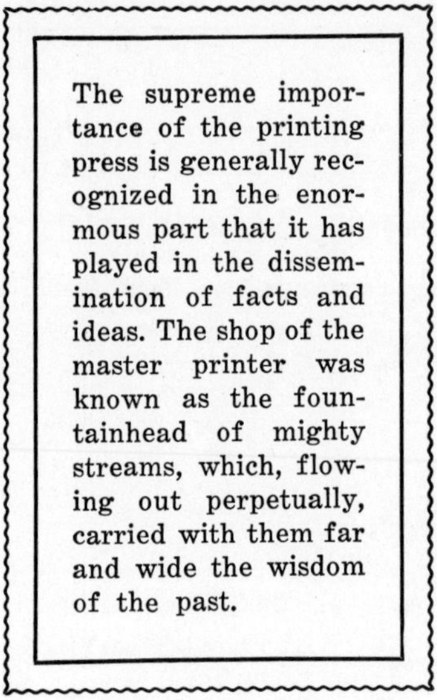

The supreme impor-
tance of the printing
press is generally rec-
ognized in the enor-
mous part that it has
played in the dissem-
ination of facts and
ideas. The shop of the
master printer was
known as the foun-
tainhead of mighty
streams, which, flow-
ing out perpetually,
carried with them far
and wide the wisdom
of the past.

FIGURE 64—AN INCORRECT MAR-
GINAL PROPORTION.

The supreme impor-
tance of the printing
press is generally rec-
ognized in the enor-
mous part that it has
played in the dissem-
ination of facts and
ideas. The shop of the
master printer was
known as the foun-
tainhead of mighty
streams, which, flow-
ing out perpetually,
carried with them far
and wide the wisdom
of the past.

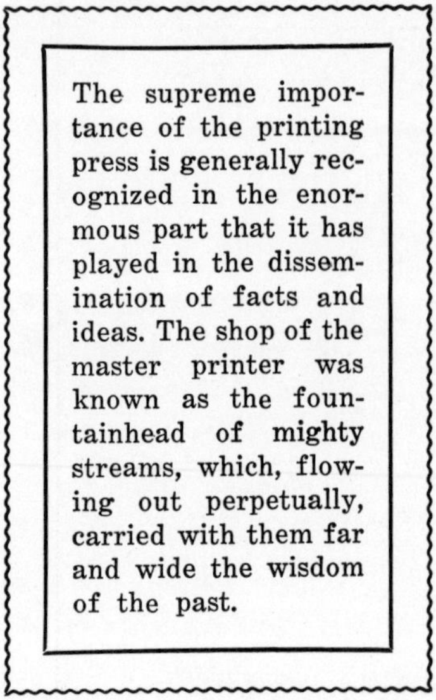

FIGURE 65—A CORRECT MARGINAL
PROPORTION.

correct marginal proportion. A correct marginal proportion is shown in Figure 65.

102. *Bleeding*—Illustrations on booklets are often "bled" —that is, so that they run off the edge of the page.

103. *The Hypotenuse Oblong* is a good page proportion which will cut without waste from standard book paper sizes. The length or width of the page is determined by an hypotenuse, which is the long side of a right angle tri-angle. When halved or doubled, the oblong remains in the same original proportion.

APPROPRIATENESS

104. *"Appropriateness"* to the printer means the correct fitting of type faces, border and decorative material to the job.

KING'S PLOWS

Are Revolutionizing Farming

Cut ground into finest particles; go over ground but once; dig thirteen inches deep; and have no obstacles

———

King's Plows, Inc.
Philadelphia

FIGURE 66—TYPE APPROPRIATE TO SUBJECT MATTER.

ROSS SECURITY CO.

MORTGAGES—BONDS
SECURITIES

CABLE BLDG.   AKRON, O.

TELEPHONE 7200

FIGURE 67—TYPE APPROPRIATE TO SUBJECT MATTER.

A bold type, which denotes strength and durability, is very appropriate for such subjects as machinery, as in Figure 66. A conservative letter is used for the broker, as shown in Figure 67. A modiste's announcement set in bold-face type would be incongruous—but the light-faced text letter used in Figure 68 is appropriate, being dainty and artistic in form.

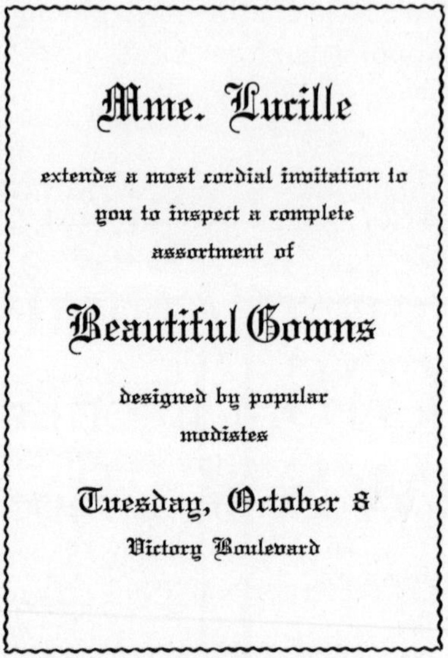

Mme. Lucille

extends a most cordial invitation to
you to inspect a complete
assortment of

Beautiful Gowns

designed by popular
modistes

Tuesday, October 8

Victory Boulevard

FIGURE 68—TYPE APPROPRIATE TO SUBJECT MATTER.

105. *Choosing the Correct Type Face*—A few general hints for choosing type faces are as follows:

1. The light-face roman cap is quite dignified and formal. Roman is appropriate for title faces, formal announcements, etc.

2. The italic is rather informal and more graceful than the roman, and is used on less serious work.

3. The text faces are formal and at the same time decorative. Heavy faces are appropriate for church use. Light-face text faces are appropriate for millinery announcements, and kindred work.

4. Gothic (or "block") finds its place on stationery and blank forms. This face has little beauty, and is a utility type.

5. Script is appropriate for composing wedding announcements, ladies' cards, and like work.

Caslon, a neutral type
Bodoni, a formal type
Garamond, an informal type
Stymie Medium, a block type
Kaufmann, an occasional type
Cooper Black, a rugged type

FIGURE 69—A TYPE CLASSIFICATION.

Type may be divided into the following classifications: neutral, formal, informal, block, occasional, and rugged.

Some of these types are shown in Figure 69. Neutral would include Binny Oldstyle and Ronaldson. Other formal faces are Bulmer, Baskerville, Scotch Roman, Century Schoolbook, and Cheltenham. To the informal list add Cloister, Goudy, Piranesi, Nicolas Cochin, and Bernhard Booklet. Among the block types are Franklin Gothic, News Gothic, Newport, and Bernhard Fashion. In addition to Cooper Black in the rugged faces are Powell, Roycroft, and occasional types include such faces as Raleigh Cursive, Romany, Pericles, Othello, American Text and Nubian.

THE LAYOUT

106. A *Layout* is the working plan for a piece of printed matter. The layout is like the architect's blueprint, and on it detailed instruction is given to the compositor—the size of the job, kind of border to be used, style and size of type, caps or lowercase, widths of lines, and so on.

107. *Advantages of the Layout*—This system of planning the job first on paper has the following advantages:

1. It gives a good idea of how the job will look when set in type.

2. It saves guesswork on the part of the compositor. In using the layout, the "trial-and-error" method of fitting both display and body type to the job is remedied.

3. Errors and inappropriate and inharmonious elements may be easily observed and corrected before the job is composed. An enormous amount of time is saved.

108. *The Layout Sheet*—Although layouts may be easily made on a piece of plain paper, the work is facilitated by using a special sheet which ruled in pica squares. This is called a "layout sheet."

109. *The Layout Procedure*—In laying out printing forms, the following procedure is a good guide to follow:

1. Draw on the layout sheet the size of stock (paper) on which the job is to be printed. Use a pica rule, and draw the lines neatly, lightly and accurately.

2. Determine the size of margins and border.

3. Analyze the copy and pick out its essential features, and determine the display lines.

4. Fit the display matter in the width of line by printing

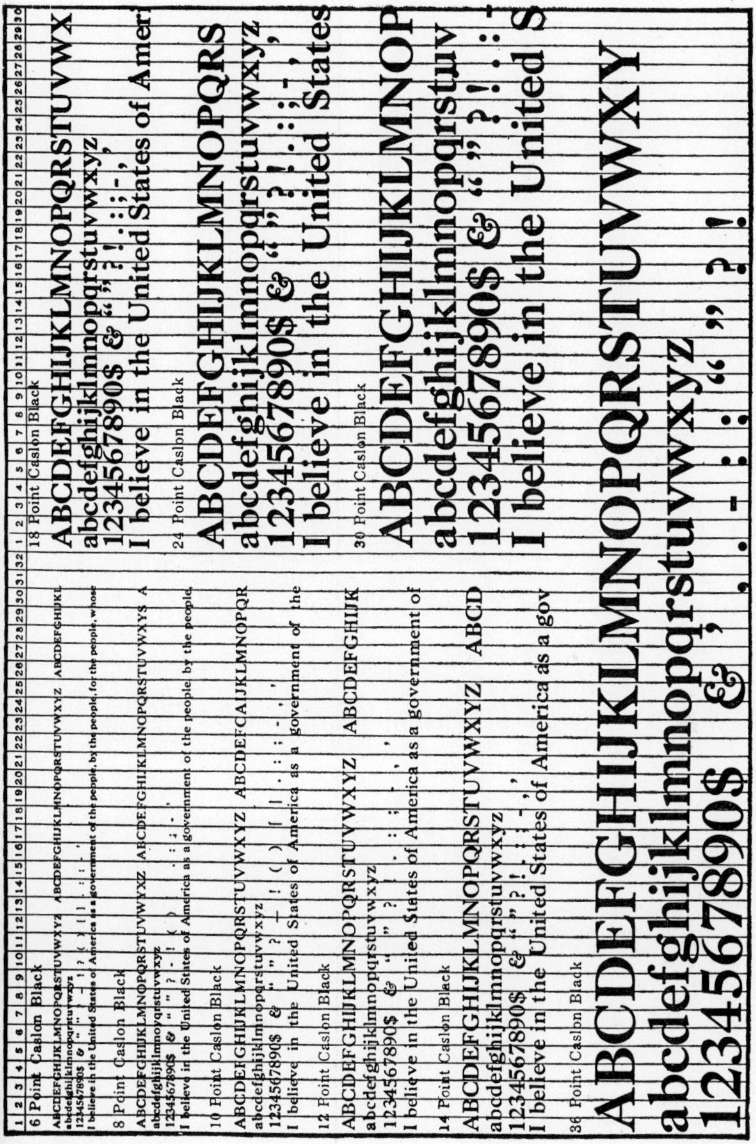

FIGURE 70—A TYPE SHEET USED FOR COPY-FITTING DISPLAY MATTER.

in by hand the wording to be emphasized. A study of the type faces in the shop from printed jobs, or the type catalog will assist in this operation.

5. Minor display lines should then be drawn on the layout sheet by the same method.

110. *The Type Sheet*—A sheet showing all fonts of type in the shop is an invaluable aid in layout work. One style is shown in Figure 70, which shows the widths of all letters and characters in each size of a series of Caslon Black, 6 to 36 point. With this sheet it is easy to ascertain just what size type will fit the determined measure. This is done by laying a rule along the measure the job is to be set (the width is indicated by the small figures on the top of the form). By comparing the number of letters on the copy and on the type sheet, the correct size to use is quickly found.

Figure 71 shows a layout, drawn and correctly marked in detail on a ruled layout sheet. The job set from this layout is shown in Figure 72.

111. A *Dummy* is a layout for a book, pamphlet or folder. The number of pages and the information for assembling are determined from this dummy.

112. *Layout Hints*—The following hints will greatly assist in layout work:

1. Do not crowd type matter.

2. The beginner should use only one family of type, and be safe.

3. Make simplicity the chief factor in the layout.

4. See that the important lines are displayed.

5. Use the period in display matter only when needed for the sense of the matter.

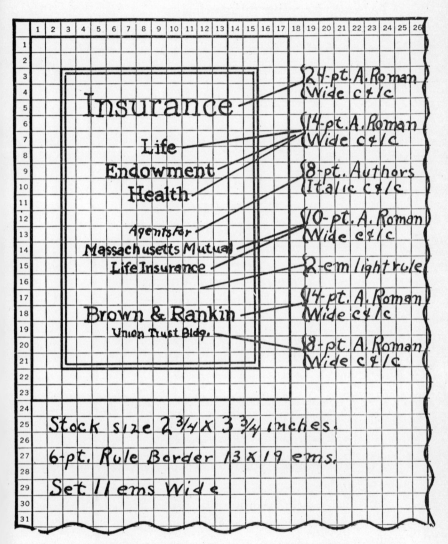

Insurance — 24-pt. A. Roman Wide c & l c

Life — 14-pt. A. Roman Wide c & l c

Endowment
Health — 8-pt. Authors Italic c & l c

Agents for
Massachusetts Mutual
Life Insurance — 10-pt. A. Roman Wide c & l c

2-em light rule

Brown & Rankin — 14-pt. A. Roman Wide c & l c

Union Trust Bldg. — 8-pt. A. Roman Wide c & l c

Stock size 2 3/4 x 3 3/4 inches.

6-pt. Rule Border 13 x 19 ems.

Set 11 ems Wide

FIGURE 71—A REPRODUCTION OF A WORKING LAYOUT.

6. Use underscoring rule sparingly.

7. Margins for book pages should decrease in this order: bottom, outside, top, inside. When one sheet is printed alone, the top and sides should be the same, the bottom slightly larger.

Insurance

Life
Endowment
Health

Agents For
**Massachusetts Mutual
Life Insurance**

————

Brown & Rankin
Union Trust Bldg.

FIGURE 72—JOB SET FROM LAYOUT IN FIGURE 71.

8. Use very small type faces sparingly, as they are very difficult to read.

9. Avoid too many groups of type matter on the same page. Do not scatter the type lines over the page; arrange in groups.

10. Avoid much decoration.

11. Use white space liberally.

12. Lowercase, being more legible than caps, should be used as much as possible.

13. Bold-face body matter should be avoided.

14. Display running into two lines or more should be broken so that each line has a meaning of its own.

15. Avoid in display matter lines of almost the same length. It is better to use the squared form of display, or long and short lines.

16. The pyramid form of display is poor; use the half-diamond style.

17. Caps may be letterspaced. Only in rare cases should lowercase be letterspaced.

18. Avoid too great a contrast between display and body matter.

19. A spot of color is often more effective than several lines or border printed in color.

20. Above all, remember that anything printed was made to be easily read.

113. *Fitting Body Matter*—Many systems of determining what size type face to use for body matter to fill a certain space are in vogue today. A general table is rather useless because of the individual difference found in type styles in all sizes. The best method is the unit count—basing the lowercase c as a unit, and having the copy typewritten to aid in determining the units. Many shops have large sheets showing regular body types in many sizes, set solid, leaded and double leaded. Sections showing page sizes may be drawn off, and an accurate estimate given on how much space a certain number of units or words will take. However, the following table will enable the estimator to roughly determine body sizes:

	Solid	2-point leaded
6 point	47	34
8 point	32	23
10 point	21	16
12 point	14	9
14 point	11	7
18 point	7	6

FIGURE 73—NUMBER OF WORDS TO SQUARE INCH.

8 point	14 picas
10 point	15 picas
12 point	18 picas
14 point	20 picas
18 point	24 picas

FIGURE 74—BEST WIDTHS TO SET BODY MATTER.

QUESTIONS FOR CLASS DISCUSSION

1. How is emphasis gained in printed matter?   89.

2. Name the three forms of display and discuss each.   90.

3. Discuss the use of one family of type in a job.   96.

4. What can you say on the use of condensed and extended faces?   98.

5. What is meant by "harmony of tone"?   97.

6. Discuss the "mathematical" and "optical" center.   99.

7. What is the rule of balance?   100.

8. What is the ratio for page margins?   101.

9. What is meant by "bleeding" an illustration?   102.

10. Name a type face appropriate for a hardware advertisement. A ladies' clothier? A doctor's billhead? A beauty-parlor announcement? A banker's letterhead? A night club?   104, 105.

11. What is advantageous in the printer's layout?   107.

12. In what ways is body matter fitted?   113.

BOOKS FOR FURTHER READING

BARTELS, "Art of Spacing," Inland Printer Co., Pages 59 to 78.

EHRLICH, "The New Typography and Modern Layouts," Frederick A. Stokes Co.

FRAZIER, "Modern Type Display," Inland Printer Co.

GRESS, "Art and Practice of Typography," Oswald Publishing Co., Pages 41 to 46, 53 to 58.

I. T. U. LESSONS, "First Steps in Job Composition," "Job Composition," "Display Composition," and "Book Composition."

TREZISE, "Design and Color in Printing," Inland Printer Co.

—— "Typography of Advertisements," Inland Printer Co., Chap. 2.

WILLIAMS, "Marking Copy for Newspaper Ad. Machines," Inland Printer Co.

CHAPTER X

COMMERCIAL PRINTING

ENVELOPE CORNER CARDS

114. The primary purpose of the envelope corner card is to notify the post office of the identity and address of the sender, to whom the letter is returned should it fail to reach its destination. The corner card is also a means of advertising.

115. *Sizes of Envelopes*—The No. $6\frac{3}{4}$ is the most used size in business envelopes. An $8\frac{1}{2}$ by 11-inch letterhead folds well to fit this size. Professional men usually favor the Executive envelope, and use the $7\frac{1}{4}$ by $10\frac{1}{2}$-inch letterhead.

	Inches
No. 5	$5\frac{1}{2}$ by $3\frac{1}{8}$
No. $6\frac{1}{4}$	6 by $3\frac{1}{2}$
No. $6\frac{3}{4}$	$6\frac{1}{2}$ by $3\frac{5}{8}$
No. 7	$6\frac{3}{4}$ by $3\frac{3}{4}$
Executive	$7\frac{1}{2}$ by $3\frac{7}{8}$
No. 9	$8\frac{7}{8}$ by $3\frac{7}{8}$
No. 10	$9\frac{1}{2}$ by $4\frac{1}{8}$
No. 11	$10\frac{3}{8}$ by $4\frac{1}{2}$
No. 12	11 by $4\frac{3}{4}$

FIGURE 75—ENVELOPE SIZES.

The popular size in the large envelope is the No. 10. The return address on social envelopes finds favor when printed on the flap.

116. *Printing Envelopes*—On very large orders (in the hundreds of thousands) envelopes are usually printed in "gangs"— meaning about 10 to 20 or more printed on a sheet at a time. These sheets are then died out in the shape of an opened envelope, and run through an envelope-making machine, which folds and glues them. Another method is making the died-out blanks first, and then running them through high-speed automatically fed presses.

117. *Typography of the Envelope*—Corner cards for envelopes should be set small—the display line seldom larger

DR. EDWARD JONES
1102 SINCLAIR BLDG.
AKRON, OHIO

FIGURE 76—AN ENVELOPE CORNER CARD FOR THE PROFESSIONAL MAN.

THE JOHNSON HARDWARE CO.
Building Materials, Tools,
Stoves, Farming Equipment
PARKERSBURG, WEST VIRGINIA

FIGURE 77—AN APPROPRIATE CORNER CARD FOR THE HARDWARE MERCHANT.

than 12-point. Ten or 15 ems is a good measure to set No. $6\frac{3}{4}$ and Executive envelopes. No. 10 envelopes may be set 20 ems wide.

Figure 76 represents a corner card for the professional man, to be printed on an Executive envelope. A hardware-store return address, for a No. 10 envelope, is shown in Figure 77.

LETTERHEADS

118. *Sizes of Letterheads*—The most-used letterhead size is $8\frac{1}{2}$ by 11 inches. Very often the half-size, or $8\frac{1}{2}$ by $5\frac{1}{2}$ inches, printed the broad way, is used for short messages. The $7\frac{1}{4}$ by $10\frac{1}{2}$-inch letterhead finds favor with professional people.

119. *Letterhead Design*—As a business or individual is often judged by stationery, great care should be taken to see that this mailed representative is neat, well-printed, and appropriate. Simplicity in design is most effective, and creates the right impression upon the reader.

120. *Letterhead Content*—A letterhead should contain the firm's or individual's name, the nature of the business, and the street address, city and state. Often the telephone number is printed, and the names of the officers of the firm.

121. *Personal Stationery*—Many different styles, sizes and typographical arrangements are found in personal stationery. A popular size, however, is the $7\frac{1}{4}$ by $10\frac{1}{2}$-inch, using the Executive envelope.

Thompson's China Shoppe

Fifth and Town Streets

Columbus, Ohio

FIGURE 78—AN APPROPRIATE LETTERHEAD.

122. *Typography of the Letterhead*—The letterhead of the professional man should be dignified and refined, and small type should be used. Decorative treatment may be considered, as shown in Figure 78.

The $8\frac{1}{2}$ by 11 inch letterhead is usually set 45 ems wide. The display line, however, should never fill this measure. The display line in letterheads must be kept in 18-point type or smaller, except in rare instances. The $7\frac{1}{4}$ by $10\frac{1}{2}$-inch letterhead should be set 40 ems wide, and the display kept below 14-point type.

CARDS

123. Both the calling card and the business card make it unnecessary for a caller to state who he is, or who he represents. This eliminates embarrassment on the part of either person.

124. *Card Stock*—The paper stock for cards usually comes to the printer already die-cut to standard sizes, packed in boxes of 500. Stock thicknesses are usually referred to, as 2-ply, 3-ply, etc. Some sizes of cards are shown in Figure 79.

CALLING CARDS

Inches

Mr. size	$3\frac{3}{16}$ by $1\frac{11}{16}$
Miss size	$2\frac{15}{16}$ by $2\frac{1}{16}$
Mrs. size	$3\frac{1}{4}$ by $2\frac{1}{4}$
Mr. and Mrs. size	$3\frac{1}{2}$ by $2\frac{1}{2}$
Juvenile size	$2\frac{1}{4}$ by $1\frac{1}{8}$
Club size	$2\frac{15}{16}$ by $1\frac{7}{16}$

BUSINESS CARDS

No. 10	$2\frac{1}{4}$ by $1\frac{11}{16}$
No. 11	$3\frac{3}{8}$ by $1\frac{7}{8}$
No. 12	$3\frac{5}{8}$ by $2\frac{1}{16}$
No. 13	$3\frac{15}{16}$ by $2\frac{5}{16}$
No. 14	$4\frac{1}{8}$ by $2\frac{9}{16}$

FIGURE 79—STANDARD CARD SIZES.

125. *Content of Cards*—The social card usually contains only the name. Very often, however, the address is printed in one lower corner of the card. Too much copy is usually

Miss Lucille Jones

FIGURE 80—A LADY'S CALLING CARD.

crowded into the business card. The firm's name, the nature of the business, the representative, the address, and perhaps the telephone number should be displayed in order.

A. S. MARTIN   C. B. LANGE

MARTIN & LANGE
STATIONERS AND
PRINTERS

REPRESENTED BY   14 JACKSON STREET
B. S. MOORE   CHICAGO

FIGURE 81—A BUSINESS CARD.

126. *Typography of the Card*—The typography of the card should be in keeping with the other printed matter of the organization. The main display line should be set in the optical center of the card. A margin of $1\frac{1}{2}$ ems is sufficient for the other matter. Type faces should naturally be kept small in composing cards. However, the amount of copy and the size of the card must determine the size of the type.

BILLHEADS AND STATEMENTS

127. *Billheads* are used by the seller to send out accounts of charges to the buyer. The billhead is mailed soon after the goods are delivered, and is regarded as a notice of payment due the sender.

128. *Statements* are for the purpose of sending out a monthly account to inform the debtor of his balance, which was payable when the billhead was sent. The word "statement" usually appears at the top of the sheet, to distinguish it from the billhead.

129. *Billhead and Statement Sizes*—Billheads and statements may be purchased already cut to size and pen ruled with perpendicular and horizontal lines. A blank space of from $2\frac{1}{2}$ to 3 inches is left at the top of the blank for imprinting the necessary copy. However, with the increasing use of the typewriter and billing machines, the plain sheet is gradually taking the place of the ruled sheet. The same sizes, however, are usually adhered to, as given in Figure 82.

BILLHEADS

$8\frac{1}{2}$ by $4\frac{2}{3}$ inches $8\frac{1}{2}$ by $9\frac{1}{3}$ inches
$8\frac{1}{2}$ by 7 inches $8\frac{1}{2}$ by 14 inches

STATEMENTS

$5\frac{1}{2}$ by $8\frac{1}{2}$ inches $4\frac{1}{8}$ by $5\frac{1}{2}$ inches
$5\frac{2}{3}$ by 11 inches $3\frac{1}{2}$ by $8\frac{1}{2}$ inches
$5\frac{1}{2}$ by $5\frac{1}{2}$ inches $5\frac{1}{2}$ by 6 inches

FIGURE 82—SIZES OF RULED BILLHEADS AND STATEMENTS.

130. *The Invoice* is similar to the billhead. It is mailed at the time of shipment of goods, so that the customer may check on the articles sent. The word "invoice" should be printed in prominent type at the head of the blank to distinguish it from similar forms. The $8\frac{1}{2}$-inch width is used for the invoice and the length varies.

131. *Typography of the Billhead*—When ruled sheets are not used, it is customary for the printer to run perpendicular

---

THE SIMPSON-ROBERTSON COMPANY

Dealers in

HIGH-GRADE GROCERIES AND MEATS

3900 North High Street   Chicago, Illinois

Sold to_____

_____   Date_____

Terms, Net Cash 30 Days

FIGURE 83—A BILLHEAD.

---

lines down the sheet as shown in Figure 83. In the first space on the left is typed the quantity; in the second, the description; and in the third and fourth spaces the price. Either leaders or lines are appropriate for the space used for addressing the billhead.

TICKETS

132. *Tickets* are used to facilitate admitting and seating audiences in public places of entertainment. There are very many kinds and styles of tickets, used for many purposes.

Theater tickets of the roll variety, each numbered, are printed on special machines in specialty plants.

133. *Sizes of Tickets*—There is no fixed and standard size for tickets. Scrap or waste stock from other jobs is often utilized, being cut to the desired size. Very often standard card stock is used. A ticket should be small enough, however, to easily fit into a man's pocketbook. They must be printed

> **"CAPTAIN OF PLYMOUTH"**
> Presented by
> **HARDING JUNIOR HIGH SCHOOL**
> Wednesday, May 9
>
> Wells Auditorium   7:30 P.M.
>
> Adults 75c   Students 25c

FIGURE 84—AN ADMISSION TICKET.

on stock sturdy enough to wear well until the entertainment. Tickets usually range in size from 2 by 3½ to 2½ by 4 inches.

134. *Content of Tickets*—Care must be taken to see that no unnecessary copy is contained in the ticket, because of its small size. This will eliminate any crowding of type. A ticket should contain only enough facts to serve its purpose as a card of admission. The following facts should be printed in this order of importance:

1. Title of presentation.
2. Organization or person giving presentation.
3. Place to be presented.
4. Day, month and year to be presented.

5. Time of day to be presented.

6. Price of admission.

135. *Typography of the Ticket*—Tickets usually look better if set with a border. Care must be taken to see that marginal proportion prevails, and that harmony exists between the type face used and the border.

When setting the ticket, the border is made up first, then side slugs are put in place for the margins between the border and the type matter. Provision is sometimes made on the left side to write in the row and seat number.

TAGS

136. *Tags* are fastened to packages, boxes, bundles, and the like to provide the necessary instructions and information concerning the shipment to postal or express employees. Tags also have a certain advertising value, as they are handled by many people.

137. *Sizes of Tags*—Tags are manufactured in many sizes, usually packed 500 in a box, either single or in gangs of four. Many styles are available with metal or heavy fiber eyelets, which safeguard them from becoming torn from the string and lost. For a slight additional cost, tags may be bought already strung with cord, or wired. A few sizes of tags are shown in Figure 85.

Size	Inches
No. 1	$2\frac{3}{4}$ by $1\frac{3}{8}$
No. 2	$3\frac{1}{2}$ by $1\frac{5}{8}$
No. 3	$3\frac{3}{4}$ by $1\frac{7}{8}$
No. 4	$4\frac{1}{2}$ by $2\frac{1}{8}$
No. 5	$4\frac{3}{4}$ by $2\frac{3}{8}$
No. 6	$5\frac{1}{4}$ by $2\frac{5}{8}$
No. 7	$5\frac{3}{4}$ by $2\frac{7}{8}$
No. 8	$6\frac{1}{4}$ by $3\frac{1}{8}$

FIGURE 85—STANDARD TAG SIZES.

138. *Tag Copy Content*—The content of tags, as shown in Figure 86, gives the name of the sender, the business, the address, and a space sufficiently large to write in the name and address of the recipient of the goods.

139. *Typography of the Tag*—The size of the tag used determines the type size. Borders are often used, and many pleasing effects are possible. The sender's name may either

FROM

NORWOOD PUBLISHING CO., INC.

PRINTERS AND BINDERS

1378 MAIN AVE.   NORWOOD, O.

FIGURE 86—A SHIPPING TAG.

head the tag, or be located at the foot. Either rule or leader lines may be utilized for writing in the name. At least 18 points must be set between the addressing lines. The words "To" and "From" used on tags is a matter of choice. The eyelet should appear at the left of the type form, as shown in the illustration.

PACKAGE LABELS

140. *Sizes of Labels*—The usual size for labels is 6 by 4 inches. The size of the label should be determined, however, by the usual size of packages made up. Labels are usually printed on paper stock that is already gummed on one side, so that they may be easily attached to the wrapper of the package.

141. *Content of the Label*—Guide lines, as shown in Figure 87, may be omitted on labels that are to be addressed on the typewriter. The label should contain the name of the sender, and the street, city, and state address. Notices are

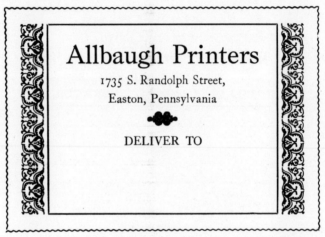

FIGURE 87—THE USE OF DECORATIVE MATERIAL ON THE PACKAGE LABEL.

frequently included to postmasters regarding the class of mail under which the package is sent.

142. *Typography of the Label*—Labels are usually set with borders, and decorative effects may be achieved, as in the accompanying illustration. Sufficient space for addressing is necessary, and any advertising matter should be subdued. Great care should be taken in composing the label, as it is second in importance only to the letter and envelope as an emissary of the user.

THE MENU

143. A *Menu* is a detailed list of dishes served at a meal. The term "menu" also embraces the restaurant "bill of fare."

144. *Sizes of Menus*—There is no set style or size for menus. The list is usually printed on heavy cover stock or

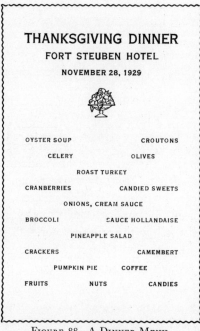

THANKSGIVING DINNER

FORT STEUBEN HOTEL

NOVEMBER 28, 1929

OYSTER SOUP		CROUTONS
CELERY		OLIVES
	ROAST TURKEY	
CRANBERRIES		CANDIED SWEETS
	ONIONS, CREAM SAUCE	
BROCCOLI		SAUCE HOLLANDAISE
	PINEAPPLE SALAD	
CRACKERS		CAMEMBERT
	PUMPKIN PIE	COFFEE
FRUITS	NUTS	CANDIES

FIGURE 88—A DINNER MENU.

cardboard, and is of a size that is easily handled. Both the single sheet and the folder style are popular.

145. *Content of Menus*—Banquet and dinner menus contain, in addition to the list of foods served, a short heading which informs the reader of the occasion of the dinner, the date, time and place, as shown in Figure 88.

146. *Typography of the Menu*—Readability is the keynote of the well-composed menu. White space is used in abundance, and large margins are created. The dinner courses are arranged in well-balanced groups in the order of their serving.

PROGRAMS

147. A *Program* informs the reader of the procedure of an entertainment, church service, exercise, or dance. The size of a program depends upon the amount of copy it contains—a program may consist of only one sheet, or a dozen pages. Advertising matter often bears the expense of printing a program, and this swells it to greater proportions. The usual page size runs from 4 by 6 to 6 by 9 inches.

148. *Program Content*—The program contains necessary information to give the audience an understanding of the procedure of the event. The following are usually given: the title of the affair, by whom it is presented, the place, the time, and a list of the participants. Acts, scenes, directors, and so on usually follow the above order.

149. *Typography of the Program*—Church programs are more in keeping with the subject if set in ecclesiastical style, which was followed by churches in the early days. Old English is patterned after the style of the hand-penned books, usually Bibles, which monks spent years in preparing. Maltese crosses (✠) and Old English types are appropriate in the composition of church printing. Red and black are appropriate church colors.

150. *Dance Programs*—This class of work is printed usually in a four-page folder style, using the title page, which gives space for the writing in of names in the two opposing middle pages.

151. *Entertainment Programs* may be composed in a great many styles. Leaders are sometimes used in setting the cast of characters, but it is better to use periods or hyphens

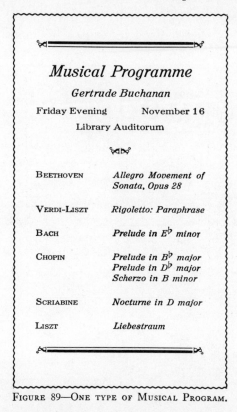

FIGURE 89—ONE TYPE OF MUSICAL PROGRAM.

spaced with em quads. A combination of caps, small caps and italic is often utilized, as in Figure 89.

HANDBILLS

152. *Sizes of Handbills*—Handbills are usually printed in sizes 6 by 9, 9 by 12, and 12 by 18 inches. Any size, however, that cuts evenly from the standard newspaper stock is suitable. Scrap stock is often utilized.

153. *Content of the Handbill*—There is a danger of getting too much copy on the handbill. It is necessary that the copy be brief and concise. Crowded and voluminous printing is

Address

— By —

Dr. Charles Poe

of Cincinnati

Stivers Auditorium

Friday, Oct. 25

Admission Free   **8 P.M.**

FIGURE 90—A SIMPLE FORM OF HAND-
BILL.

not easily read, and will not convey the message to the majority of the readers.

154. *Typography of the Handbill*—Bold type in a legible face is appropriate in the composition of the handbill. Borders are usually omitted. Brass rules are often used to square up the copy and divide it into units, as shown in Figure 90.

Margins are made one-half inch for the 6 by 9-inch size, and slightly larger for the bigger sizes.

ANNOUNCEMENTS

155. An *Announcement* is a formal printed or engraved notice, usually mailed, of an event which will occur, or has already occurred.

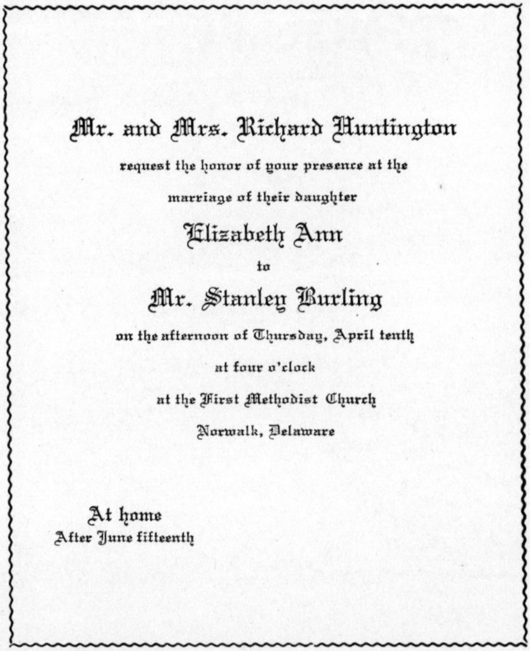

Mr. and Mrs. Richard Huntington

request the honor of your presence at the

marriage of their daughter

Elizabeth Ann

to

Mr. Stanley Burling

on the afternoon of Thursday, April tenth

at four o'clock

at the First Methodist Church

Norwalk, Delaware

At home
After June fifteenth

FIGURE 91—A WEDDING ANNOUNCEMENT.

156. *Social and Wedding Announcements*—The better class of wedding announcements are produced by the copperplate engraving method. A less expensive method is by thermography and letterpress printing.

157. *Advertising Announcements* range in size from a small card to an elaborately colored and designed broadside. The announcement plays a very important part in direct mail advertising.

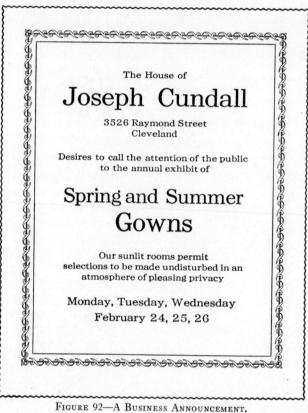

The House of

Joseph Cundall

3526 Raymond Street
Cleveland

Desires to call the attention of the public
to the annual exhibit of

Spring and Summer
Gowns

Our sunlit rooms permit
selections to be made undisturbed in an
atmosphere of pleasing privacy

Monday, Tuesday, Wednesday
February 24, 25, 26

FIGURE 92—A BUSINESS ANNOUNCEMENT.

158. *Announcement Stock*—Mailing sets, consisting of folders, sheets, or card, with envelopes to match, are occasionally used for business announcements. Social announcements are printed on the first page of a four-page folder, which matches a set of two envelopes. One envelope holds the announcement, which is placed in a slightly larger one, on which the addressing is done for mailing. The usual size is 5 by 7 inches when folded. A high grade stock of medium finish and heavy weight is used. Blind embossing often forms a panel on which the type matter is finished.

159. *Typography of the Announcement*—Social announcements are printed in a light-face text type, script, or any other appropriate announcement type, of which there are a great many. No border is used, and the copy is composed of a few brief facts. Wide margins are used, as shown in Figure 91. Twelve and 18-point type is usually used.

The type used in the business announcement should be in harmony with the subject of the mailing piece. Both plain and decorative borders are used. Most announcements of this nature are printed on distinctive cover stocks in colors.

GREETING CARDS

160. *Greeting Cards* are used to send the compliments of the season, as on Christmas, New Year's Day, Easter, or on birthdays, to express one's feeling to a friend or acquaintance.

The custom of sending greeting cards originated in England about the year 1846. The greeting card, as a Christmas offering, at once found favor with the royalty, and later the middle classes, and grew finally to its immense proportions.

Louis Prang, a lithographer of Boston, who is also given credit for the introduction of art education into the public schools of America, published the first greeting cards in this country in 1874.

Greeting cards are engraved, lithographed and printed.

Thermography is used, imitating engraving. Illustrations are popular, often in as many as ten colors. Many original designs, especially appropriate to the sender, are used.

161. *Typography of the Greeting Card*—Although rather more expensive in most cases, the individual printed greeting

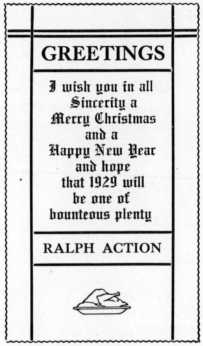

GREETINGS

I wish you in all
Sincerity a
Merry Christmas
and a
Happy New Year
and hope
that 1929 will
be one of
bounteous plenty

RALPH ACTION

FIGURE 93—A TYPOGRAPHIC GREETING
CARD.

card is most popular. Often the whole of one's family is pictured with their words of yuletide cheer. Original designs should be determined, and color used, as shown in Figures 93 and 94. The size must be determined from the copy, illustration, and the size of the mailing sets which may be purchased from any paper merchant.

MAY the Great :: Holiday Spirit be very considerate of you this year

JOHN ABEL

Steubenville, O.
1930-31

FIGURE 94—A TYPOGRAPHIC CHRIST-MAS GREETING.

POSTERS AND WINDOW CARDS

162. A *Poster* is a sign, intended to be affixed to a wall or sign board to convey a public announcement. The window card is printed on heavy cardboard, and is placed in store windows for advertising purposes. Street-car cards are printed on cardboard 21 by 11 inches, to fit the standard frames built into the sides of street cars and buses.

163. *Sizes of Posters and Window Cards*—Posters are printed in sizes 28 by 42, 21 by 28 and 14 by 21 inches. These sizes are called full-size, half-size, and quarter-size, respectively. Very large posters are printed in sections 29 by 39 inches, and are pasted in order to standard size billboards.

Window cards are printed in smaller size than the poster. The size usually depends on the amount of the copy, being

EXHIBITION
OF
HIGH SCHOOL PRINTING
WEEK OF MAY 3
NORWOOD HIGH SCHOOL

FIGURE 95—A POSTER.

one that cuts evenly from stock $22\frac{1}{2}$ by $28\frac{1}{2}$ inches. A stiff stock must be used to keep the card upright.

164. *Content of Window Cards*—The message printed on window cards should necessarily be brief, as it must catch the eye and deliver the message quickly. This is illustrated in Figure 95. Very often interesting quotations, poems, and the like are printed in small poster form, similar to Figure 96. The type composition of school shops is displayed in this fashion in contests and exhibitions.

165. *Typography of the Window Card*—Posters and window cards must be set in type large enough to be read from a distance. The type dress must be in keeping with the subject. Window cards are composed both the long and short

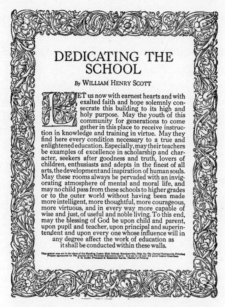

FIGURE 96—A POSTER SHOWING SCHOOL
TYPOGRAPHY.

way of the stock, depending upon the most advantageous proportion.

ADVERTISEMENTS

166. The most important features of the advertisement are (1) its ability to attract the eye; (2) its ability to hold the reader's attention by being legible; and (3) its ability to cause the reader to act favorably.

167. *Measurements of Advertisements*—Column widths are ordinarily 12, 12½ or 13 ems wide, depending on the press and the stereotyping equipment used. Column widths must be taken into consideration in determining the measures to set advertisements that are larger than one column wide. Column rule is invariably a hair-line cast on a 6-point body, centered.

"Agate lines" are usually used in the measurement of small advertisements. An agate line is $5\frac{1}{2}$ points; 14 lines to the inch. Larger advertisements are charged for at certain rates for one-eighth, one-quarter, one-half and full pages. Some newspapers and magazines sell space by the inch.

168. A "*Cut-off Rule*" or "advertising rule" is used to divide one advertisement from another in newspapers. The cut-off rules are usually the basis for measurement: a 3-inch advertisement, then, would measure 3 inches from one cut-off rule to the one below it.

Widths to compose advertisements are shown in Figure 97 below:

Size in Columns	2	3	4	5	6	7	8
12-em columns..........	$24\frac{1}{2}$	37	$49\frac{1}{2}$	62	$74\frac{1}{2}$	87	$99\frac{1}{2}$
12½-em columns........	$25\frac{1}{2}$	$38\frac{1}{2}$	$51\frac{1}{2}$	$64\frac{1}{2}$	$77\frac{1}{2}$	$90\frac{1}{2}$	$103\frac{1}{2}$
13-em columns	$26\frac{1}{2}$	40	$53\frac{1}{2}$	67	$80\frac{1}{2}$	94	$107\frac{1}{2}$

FIGURE 97—WIDTHS OF ADVERTISEMENTS.

169. *Typography of Advertisements*—In setting advertisements, the border is built up first, then the side margin slugs are set in place. In setting advertisements that are in half-pica measures, the 6 points of odd space must be taken up in these side margins between the border and the type matter. Type matter is seldom composed in half measures.

Where an advertisement is to be printed on a page with others, harmonious border must be used to give a pleasing effect.

Advertisements attract attention especially when they are easy to read. This should be kept in mind when laying-out.

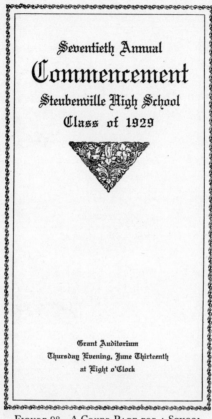

Seventieth Annual
Commencement
Steubenville High School
Class of 1929

Grant Auditorium
Thursday Evening, June Thirteenth
at Eight o'Clock

FIGURE 98—A COVER PAGE FOR A SCHOOL COMMENCEMENT PROGRAM.

TITLE AND COVER PAGES

170. The *Title Page* of a book or pamphlet is a description of the work, the publisher's imprint, the date of issue, and other information that is necessary.

Cover pages, as a rule, contain less copy than the title pages. Usually only the title of the book and the name of the author appear. Cover pages for programs present the

ANNUAL
REPORT

of the STEUBENVILLE
PUBLIC SCHOOLS

For the Year 1928-1929

THE STEUBENVILLE PUBLIC SCHOOLS
Steubenville, Ohio

FIGURE 99—A COVER FOR A BOOKLET.

name of the presentation, by whom it is given, the place, the date, and often the time—as shown in Figure 98.

Small booklets do not always contain title pages, so the necessary information is given on the cover page, as illustrated in Figure 99.

171. *Typography of the Cover Page*—Legibility and simple form is the keynote in composing cover pages and title pages. The beginner in printing must avoid the fantastic designs found on some of the fiction work of this time. Care must be taken to see that the margins are planned with care. The typography must be in keeping with the subject matter.

FIGURE 100—A TYPOGRAPHICAL
DESIGN ON A BOOKPLATE.

FIGURE 101—THE USE OF A STOCK
ELECTRO ON THE BOOKPLATE.

BOOK PLATES

172. A *Book Plate* is a label placed in a book to show its ownership. The better book plates are impressions from a copper or wood engraving, but etchings and typographical designs are used to a great extent.

Book plates originated in Germany in the fifteenth century. The earliest known printed copy was used in the year

1480. The pictorial or allegorical designs have displaced the old style coat-of-arms.

173. *Content of the Book Plate*—It is the custom to print the Latin words "Ex Libris," meaning "from the books," with the name of the owner on the book plates. Either engravings or typographical designs are used. Figure 100 presents an example of the typographical design. An electrotype of a stock engraving is shown in Figure 101.

174. *Typography of the Book Plate*—Book plates are printed in many different sizes and shapes. The size should be small enough, however, to paste inside the front cover of a book. Book plates are usually printed on gummed stock.

Many original and beautiful designs are possible in designing book plates.

RULE FORMS

175. *Ruling Machines*—The colored lines on most blank books, index cards, school tablets, statement blanks and kindred work are pen-ruled on special machines designed for this purpose.

The principle of the ruling machine is very unlike that of letterpress printing. The paper is either automatically or hand-fed between a number of endless strings and a flannel belt. The paper is carried in this manner under specially constructed steel pens, which do the ruling. These pens are fed with a liquid ink through a number of loosely twisted cords called "zephyrs," one end of which is fastened on the pen, and the other coming in contact with a strip of woolen cloth lying in a reservoir of ink. Figure 102 illustrates an automatically fed ruling machine.

Several colors may be ruled in one feeding by having different colors of ink in the reservoirs. A "striker" lifts the pens and drops them in the desired places as the sheet travels through the machine. "Dual machines" strike the cross lines and down lines at one feeding. "Quadruple machines" rule the cross and down lines on both sides of the sheet at one feeding through the machine. "Disk" ruling machines transfer the ink from a fountain to the paper by

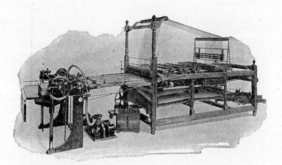

FIGURE 102—AN AUTOMATICALLY FED RULING MACHINE.

means of a revolving disk. Counting, slitting, and perforating attachments may be added to the machines.

176. *Letterpress Rule Forms*—When setting rule forms similar to Figure 103, the heading is composed first. Then each column is completely set, working from left to right. All necessary pieces of brass rule, quads and furniture should be collected before the composition is started. Bevel-faced rule should be used for the rules the full width of the form. This will insure a good joint with the down rules.

177. Rule forms are often printed in two impressions— one impression for the cross rules and type matter, and another for the down rules. "Work-and-twist" forms are printed in the same way—the stock is cut double, and the two forms are placed head-to-head. After one impression is made, the sheet is twisted in such a manner that the next impression is printed over the one preceding.

178. *Tabular Quadrules* are similar to quads, and have a rule printing surface on the bottom. These are used in place

ASSIGNMENTS FOR SCHOOL PAPER

FOR WEEK BEGINNING_____ 19__

Check If In	SUBJECT OF ARTICLE TO BE WRITTEN	See the Following for Information	Amount of Words	Due 8:30 on Morning of	ASSIGNED TO THE STUDENT NAMED BELOW
	Advertising				
	Alumni Notes				
	Art Department				
	Assembly (coming)				
	Athletics				
	Band				
	Biology Club				
	Boy Scouts				
	Cafeteria				
	Circulation				
	Commercial Club				
	Custodians				
	Dramatic Club				
	Editorial				
	Editorial				
	English Club				
	Exchanges				
	Glee Clubs				
	Girl Reserves				
	Hikers Club				
	Health Club				
	Health Dept.				
	Household Arts Dept.				
	Jokes				
	Literary				
	Manual Training				
	Mechanical Drawing				
	Music Department				
	Office				
	Orchestra				
	Rooms 109, 200, 201				
	Rooms 202, 203, 204				
	Rooms 205, 206, 208				
	Rooms 302, 303, 304				
	Rooms 305, 306				
	Rooms 307, 308, 309				
	Science Club				

FIGURE 103—A RULE FORM.

of separate quads and brass rule. Quadrules are made in 12-, 18-, and 24-point sizes, cut in wides of 12-, 18-, 24-, 30-,

36-, 48-, 60-, and 72-pica ems. The use of these quadrules saves much time in composing rule forms. Typotabular Squares, resembling 6-point em quads with pointed tops, are handy accessories in the composition of rule work.

QUESTIONS FOR CLASS DISCUSSION

1. Discuss the composition of envelope corner cards. 114–117.

2. What can you say about the setting of letterheads? 118–120, 122.

3. What particular copy should the card contain? 125.

4. Differentiate between the billhead, statement, and invoice. 127–130.

5. Discuss the copy content intended for tickets, tags, labels and menus. 134, 138, 141, 145.

6. Discuss the composition of programs. 148, 149.

7. What can you say on the setting of handbills, social announcements, and greeting cards? 154, 158, 159, 161.

8. Discuss typographically window cards and posters. 163, 165.

9. Why must column widths be kept in mind in setting advertisements? 167.

10. Differentiate between a cover page and a title page. 170.

11. Explain briefly the action of a ruling machine. 175.

12. What procedure is followed in setting rule forms? 176.

13. What is a work-and-twist form? 177.

14. What material facilitates the composition of rule forms? 178.

BOOKS FOR FURTHER READING

GRESS, "Art and Practice of Typography," Oswald Publishing Co.

I. T. U. LESSONS, "Job Units."

Mergenthaler Linotype Co., "Manual of Linotype Typography."

HACKLEMAN, "Commercial Engraving and Printing."

CHASE, "The Romance of Greeting Cards."

TREZISE, "Typography of Advertisements."

BARTELS, "The Art of Spacing."

DE VINNE, "Title Pages."

PLEGER, "Paper Ruling."

Chapter XI

MECHANICAL TYPECASTING

179. *Composing Machines*—Most of the type matter set today is done on mechanical composing machines, some of which cast the type in lines, and others in individual types. Other machines cast type to be set from cases by hand in the usual manner.

These mechanical typecasting machines are known as Linotypes, Intertypes and Linographs; Monotypes, and Ludlow Typographs.

180. *Advantages of Mechanical Typecasting Machines* are many: (1) they make possible four to five times the speed of hand composition; (2) no distribution of type by hand, as dead matter is melted over again into pigs of type metal and fed into the machines again to cast more type; (3) new type for each job, insuring a sharp, clean print; (4) ease of handling when in slug form; and (5) recasting the jobs several times to print in "gangs," that is, printing many of the same job at one time on a large sheet.

181. *Keyboard Linecasting Machines*—The Linotype, Intertype, and Linograph machines consist of four main parts: the keyboard, the magazine, the casting mechanism, and the distributing mechanism.

182. *The Keyboard*—The sole duty of the linotype man is to operate the keyboard. As he taps the keys of the power-driven keyboard, ① "matrices" are released from the "magazine" ② and fall in order in the "assembling elevator," ③ which is the "stick" of the machine.[1]

After the operator has set one line of matrices, he presses the "assembling elevator lever," ④ which raises the "assembling elevator" ③ and delivers the line of matrices to the casting mechanism. The operator is then finished with this line, and immediately starts to set the next.

A *Matrix* is a small piece of brass which acts as a mold in casting the line. Matrices 30-point and smaller are of the two-letter variety, as shown in Figure 104, which illustrates the actual size. By moving a small lever on the assembling elevator, the operator has a choice of two styles of faces from the same matrix.

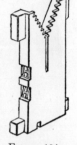

FIGURE 104—
A LINOTYPE
MATRIX.

Spacebands are used between words on the linecasting machine. These are made up of two wedges. One is held rigid in the machine, while the other is forced upward. This makes the spaceband gradually wider. In this way all lines of matrices are justified automatically by the machine, as well as evenly spaced between words. Figure 105 shows a line of matrices spaced by the spacebands.

The *Magazine* ② is the flat receptacle tapering in shape on the upper part of the machine. One to eight magazines are contained on a machine, according to the make and model. Shifting from one magazine to another for the composition of various type sizes is a simple matter, and mixing of matrices from any two magazines is possible, allowing the composition of roman, bold face, roman italic, bold italic, and small caps to be composed.

183. *The Casting Mechanism*—The line of matrices and spacebands, upon being delivered to the casting mechanism,

[1] Figures in circles refer to parts marked in Fig. 106.

is lowered by the "first elevator" ⑪ between two jaws, where the line faces the "mold." ⑤ Molten type metal is forced into this mold from the rear, the slug is cast, and instantly cools.

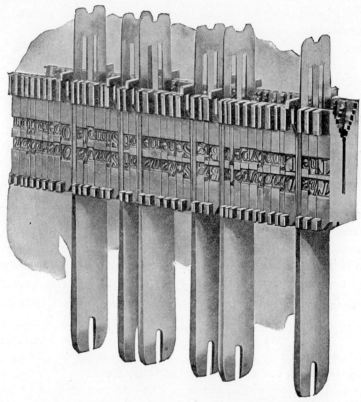

FIGURE 105—A LINE OF MATRICES JUSTIFIED WITH SPACEBANDS.

As the slug is ejected from the mold, it is trimmed on the sides and bottom, and is delivered to the "galley." ⑩

Molds are adjustable to cast varying lengths and thickness of lines. Machines are equipped to cast either 24½-, 30- or

FIGURE 106—A PHANTOM VIEW OF A LINOTYPE MACHINE SHOWING THE PATH OF THE MATRICES THROUGH THE MACHINE.

42-pica measures in maximum sizes on one slug. Wider lines are made up of "butted" slugs—two or more for each line.

184. *The Distributing Mechanism*—After the line is cast,

FIGURE 107—INTERTYPE WITH SIDE UNITS.

the matrices and spacebands are separated, the latter being carried to the "spaceband box," ⑥ located directly above the assembling elevator. The "second elevator" ⑦ descends from the top of the machine, and the matrices are shifted from the first elevator, their teeth engaging with the teeth on the second elevator bar. The second elevator then returns to the top of the machine above the magazines, where the matrices are shifted to the "distributor box." ⑨ The distrib-

FIGURE 108—MODEL 30 LINOTYPE.

utor box feeds the matrices singly to the "distributor screws," ⑧ which carry them along the "distributor bar," which consists of a grooved rail, the teeth of the matrices aligning with and adhering to the rail. The teeth on the distributor bar vary in number and arrangement at different points along the bar, where the matrices, meeting the correct combination of grooves, drop back into the channels whence they came.

Faces of slug lines are cast in sizes from 5-point to condensed 60-point. Leading is accomplished by casting a small face on a larger body. To correct errors a new line must be cast. Corrections must be made by casting a new line of type.

Border, rule and decorative material may be cast up to 30 or 42 picas in length on the linecasting machines from strips of brass called "matrix slides." Single border matrices are also used.

185. *Hand-Set Matrices*—Late models of the Linotype and the Intertype line-casting machines have attachments that allow for the composing of matrices from cases by hand, in a special composing stick. This stick of matrices, forming a line, is placed into the regular keyboard machine and lines are cast from matrices too wide to be run into the magazines.

186. An *Automatic Quadding Device* is provided on some models of linecasting machines, allowing lines to be automatically centered, or set flush right or flush left, which saves time in keyboarding the blank spaces.

187. *The All-Purpose Linotype*—The "APL," as it is called, casts slug lines of type 42 picas long, in any face size from 5- to 144-point. Matrices are set by hand in a special stick, and placed in the machine manually. After casting, the matrices are distributed into the cases.

In addition to slug lines, individual characters can be cast in lines, leaving space between letters so that they can be cut apart, and placed in cases for regular composition by hand.

The APL also produces borders from blocks so designed that one side casts rule or border, and the other side casts

FIGURE 109—AN ALL-PURPOSE LINOTYPE.

spacing material either high or low, and in any body size from 6- to 72-point, in lengths of 42 picas.

Four molds are contained in the mold disc on the APL,

which can be changed, if necessary, for various sizes of type. Large types, however, such as the 144-point size, can be cast with the face "overhanging" on a 72-point slug. This overhang is supported by underpinning slugs, cast on the same machine.

The APL may be equipped with a saw trimmer to cut lines to the desired length, and with a high-speed cutter which surfaces the face of the type lines to insure good printing quality. Italic faces are made on slanting matrices in three different angles: 12, 15 and 22 degrees. This allows each italic letter to be put at its own proper angle, and avoids distortion when these characters conform to a uniform angle.

Other features of the APL include: controlled alignment of faces on various sized slugs, pre-cooled slugs (water cooled) which can be picked up immediately by the operator after casting, automatic recasting at various speeds, provision for a convenient work table, composition of matrices with the casting-side up, and the ability to cast from regular linecasting machine matrices.

188. *The Teletypesetter*—This linecasting machine attachment is an apparatus for automatically controlling Linotype or Intertype machines by means of a perforated ribbon, or tape.

The "perforator" machine is operated like a typewriter to prepare the tape at speeds up to six lines a minute. The "operating" unit, attached to the linecasting machine, is controlled by the perforated tape.

At present being primarily a newspaper composing device, the perforated tape may be passed through printing telegraph transmitters to send in code to distant points where duplicate tapes may be prepared on teletype perforators for use on linecasting machines.

Measures up to 30 picas, in sizes of type from $5\frac{1}{2}$- to 12-point may be set, and full use of two-letter matrices may be had.

FIGURE 110—A TELETYPESETTER ATTACHED TO THE KEYBOARD
OF A LINECASTING MACHINE.

189. *The Ludlow Typograph* is a system of casting display lines of type with hand-set matrices.

The Ludlow operator picks up four or five matrices successively between his fingers and sets them in his stick. Distribution of the matrices is done in the same quick manner. As the line is cast in one piece, hairline justification is not necessary.

190. *Method of Ludlow Composition*—The work on the Ludlow is done by setting brass matrices in a specially constructed stick. These matrices are locked in the stick with

FIGURE 111—MATRICES SET IN A LUDLOW STICK, AND
THE PRODUCT OF THE MACHINE.

a thumb screw, as shown in Figure 111. The stick is then placed in a caster, where all large type lines are cast on a 12-point body. Type faces over 12 points are cast with an overhang, and centered on the slug like the letter T. The overhang is built up with low cast slugs, which are made on the same caster. When sizes smaller than 12-point are composed, a 6-point mold is available.

FIGURE 112—A 60-PICA LUDLOW LINE, CAST IN THREE SECTIONS.

The Ludlow is equipped to cast 21- or 22½-pica lines. Smaller measures must be cut to the desired measure on a saw-trimmer. Lines longer than the above measures, up to 105 picas, are cast in sections, but are justified in the full long measure as one line. This is illustrated in Figure 112.

To correct errors, an entirely new line, or section of a line, must be recast.

Sizes of Ludlow Matrices—The sizes of matrices available for the Ludlow range from 6- to 72-point. Eighty-four point

FIGURE 113—THE LUDLOW CASTER AND MATRIX CABINETS.

capitals may be cast, and 144-point to 220-point characters may be cast length-wise on the slug. Rules are engraved on

FIGURE 114—LUDLOW ITALIC MATRICES
SET IN THE SPECIAL ITALIC STICK.

the backs of the matrices which act as nicks to aid in composition and to distinguish between different fonts.

Ludlow Italic Faces are full-kerning in design, and are cast from slanting matrices cut on a 17° angle. A special italic stick is used with italic spaces and quads, as shown in Figure 114. This method of casting produces a close-fitting italic letter, with kerns that are unbreakable.

Burnishing Sluglines—For printing on coated paper, the larger sizes of Ludlow typefaces must be smoothed. This can be accomplished by rubbing the lines over a taut piece of emery cloth attached to the caster table. The Ludlow Super-surfacer accomplishes this mechanically with a power-driven, precision milling head cutter.

Ludlow Ruleform Composition is produced from hand-set ruleform matrices. By a simple interlocking principle, the down-rules in a form are locked into position, eliminating breaks and insuring alignment.

Special Composing Sticks further speed up the work in composing Ludlow matrices. The self-quadding and self-centering sticks eliminate the placing of spacing materials on either side of a centered line, or after flush left lines.

191. The *Elrod* casts leads, slugs, and line borders in strips, and thick slugs, 36 points in thickness, which are used as metal furniture. The machine is automatically operated, and cuts the material to point sizes as required. Elrod leads and slugs may be used in building up overhanging Ludlow lines.

192. The *Monotype System* casts single types from hard type metal and sets them in justified lines. The Monotype also casts type for cases which is almost identical with foundry type. Leads and slugs, rule, border both in strip material and individual types, and metal furniture may be cast on the various machines.

193. *Monotype Parts*—The Monotype system of straight matter type composition consists of two separate parts: the "keyboard," and the "composing machine" or caster.

194. The *Monotype Keyboard* contains five alphabets, the keys being arranged like that of a standard typewriter. Certain keys are provided to control the spacing and justification of lines.

When a key is struck by the operator, two holes are punched in a roll of paper ribbon. At the same time the width of the letter struck is recorded on a "justifying scale." As succeeding characters are struck, the ribbon moves forward and more perforations are made. The thickness of each succeeding letter is added to the first. When the line is almost filled, the operator is notified by a bell. Noticing the recorded total width of all the letters in the line, the operator touches two keys, and the justification of that particular line is taken care of, and the next line is begun.

195. *Monotype Spacing*—The Monotype is self-spacing, as the width of letter, or "set size" of all characters in the same font bears a fixed relation to the em. The basic letter of the font, which is the M, is divided into 18 equal parts, and one of these parts is used as the unit of measure in determining the width of each character in the font. More than 200 widths of spaces may be had on the Monotype, and the spaces in each line are uniform in size.

The Monotype keyboard is operated by compressed air, and the speed of operation is limited only to that of the operator. The paper ribbon, which is about four inches wide, is called the "controller ribbon," because it controls the action of the composing machine. Figure 115 pictures a Monotype Keyboard. The justifying scale is on a level with the operator's eyes.

As the controller ribbon is run into the composing machine backwards, the width of the spaces can be determined at the keyboard after the line is set.

FIGURE 115—A MONOTYPE KEYBOARD.

196. *Monotype Casters*—The Monotype Casters are made in several styles: composition machines, material-making machines, type and rule machines, and the Giant caster. Various equipment makes the casting of type in justified lines from 5- to 18-point, single characters for cases from 18- to 36-point, and leads, slugs, and borders—all on one machine.

197. *The Monotype Composition Machine*—This caster makes type from 5- to 18-point, and sets them in justified lines. In the smaller sizes, three faces can be cast from the same "matrix case," as roman, italic, and bold face. Combinations of different type faces may be cast and composed, and all align at the bottom of the letters.

Corrections can be made by the hand compositor. This releases both the keyboard and caster for productive work.

Copy can be fitted on the monotype composition machine to take up a certain amount of pages of a predetermined size by increasing the space slightly between the letters. Also, if leading is found to be necessary, this can be accomplished by merely casting the type on a larger body.

The Monotype is especially adapted to the composition of tabular matter. Several sections in a line may be justified independently of each other, and rules may be set in later by hand. Difficult tabular matter is set as quickly as straight matter.

The controller ribbons may be saved for future runs. This saves the cost of extra keyboard work on reruns.

Lines may be justified on the Monotype up to 65 picas wide. A 90-pica line can be cast by using a large scale.

It is often necessary to run type around irregular engravings. In Monotype composition, a quadded space is left for engravings, and after being routed down to the correct height, the printing plate is nailed fast to this base.

No other type-casting system provides as many varieties and sizes as does the Monotype. More than 3,000 faces and

FIGURE 116—A MONOTYPE COMPOSITION MACHINE.

sizes are available. Matrices may be rented from a "Matrix Library" conducted by the manufacturers.

How the Composing Machine Works—The action of the composing machine is explained as follows: The controller ribbon is first placed in the composing machine. As the ribbon passes over a tracker, similar to that of a pianola, compressed air is forced through the holes in the ribbon and directs the

FIGURE 117—A MONOTYPE MATRIX CASE.

action of a "matrix case," which contains 225 matrices. A "comb" of matrices, which fits into the matrix case, is shown in Figure 118. At each revolution of the machine, the matrix

FIGURE 118—MONOTYPE CELLULAR MATRICES IN A COMB.

case stops at a predetermined position over a mold, and a letter is cast. The machine casts small types at a speed of 150 a minute.

The justification on the Monotype composing machine is accomplished by the action of an automatically shifting

FIGURE 119a—A MONOTYPE MATERIAL MAKER.

wedge, which is directed by the last four perforations in each line punched in the controller ribbon.

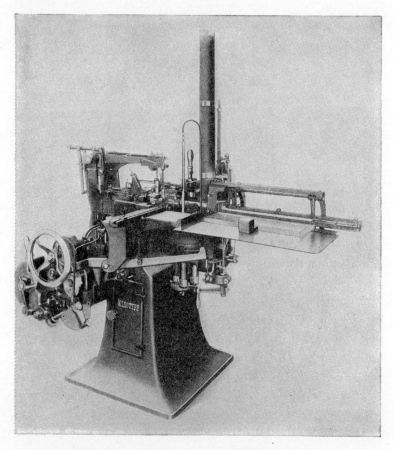

FIGURE 119b—A TYPE AND RULE MONOTYPE CASTER.

198. *The Monotype Material Maker* casts strips of leads, slugs and borders from 1-point to 12-points in thickness. This caster makes spacing material so quickly and cheaply

FIGURE 119c—A MONOTYPE GIANT CASTER.

that there is no gain in distributing the material after a job of printing is run—the entire form is thrown into the melting furnace for making up pigs, which are fed into the casting machine. This spacing material can be cut to desired sizes on the machine.

199. *The Type and Rule Caster*—This machine is for the purpose of making type in sizes from 5- to 36-point, which is placed in cases to be composed by hand. Flat or cellular matrices are placed in a holder, which is thrust into the casting mechanism to make the type. An extra attachment allows this machine to cast leads, slugs and rule.

200. *The Giant Caster* makes type in sizes from 14- to 72-point, as well as furniture, leads, slugs, spaces and quads.

200a. *The Monotype-Thompson Typecaster* is a type-founding machine capable of making single types from 5- to 48-point, ornaments, borders, quads, spaces, hollow quotation quads, corner quads and tabular quadrules in either hard or regular non-distribution system typemetal. Speeds up to 150 characters a minute are possible, and matrix and mold changes are quickly made. This machine will cast single types from matrices of all other linecasting or typecasting machines.

QUESTIONS FOR CLASS DISCUSSION

1. Name four linecasting machines.   179.
2. Name five advantages of mechanical typesetting machines over hand composition.   180.
3. Name the four main parts of a line-casting machine and tell the function of each.   181, 183, 184.
4. What is a spaceband?   182.
5. What is a magazine?   182.
6. What is meant by a mold?   183.

7. What type sizes are possible on a linecasting machine?   184. An APL?   187.

8. What is meant by an "overhang" on the APL and the Ludlow?   187, 190.

9. Explain how the teletypesetter works.   188.

10. Explain how the Ludlow operator casts type.   190.

11. What is an Elrod?   191.

12. Explain the operation of a Monotype keyboard and composition caster.   194, 197.

13. Name three other Monotype machines, and tell how they work, and what they produce.   198, 199, 200.

14. Explain the product of a Monotype-Thompson typecaster. 200a.

BOOKS FOR FURTHER READING

ROGERS, JOHN L. "Linotype Instruction Book," Mergenthaler Linotype Co.

THOMPSON, JOHN S. "Mechanism of the Linotype," Inland Printer Co.

MERGENTHALER LINOTYPE Co., "Linotype Keyboard Operation."

SINCLAIR, "The Intertype," Inland Printer Co.

THOMPSON, "History of Composing Machines," Inland Printer Co.

CHAPTER XII

LOCK-UP AND IMPOSITION

After the revise proof of a printing form has been checked, the type matter is ready to "go to press." The necessary equipment for this procedure follows:

201. The *Imposing Table* consists of a level, smooth stone- or iron-topped table on which forms are locked for the press.

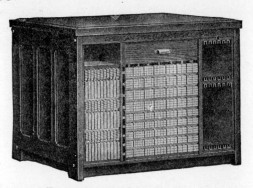

FIGURE 120—AN IMPOSING TABLE.

Usually storage space is contained under the surface for lock-up equipment, as shown in Figure 120.

202. The *Chase* is an iron or steel frame which holds the type form in position on the bed of the printing press. The size of any chase is determined by the inside measurement, as 10 by 15 or 12 by 18 inches. A chase is shown in Figure 124.

203. *Quoins and Quoin Keys*—Quoins are small iron tools which act as wedges to hold the type form in the chase. Two forms of quoins, the Hempel and the Wickersham, are shown in Figures 121 and 122.

204. *Spacing Material for Lock-Up*—Wood furniture is usually used in locking up type forms in the chase. Reglet is

FIGURE 121—HEMPEL QUOINS AND QUOIN KEY.

FIGURE 122—WICKERSHAM QUOINS AND QUOIN KEY.

inserted on each side of the quoins to protect the furniture and to keep the quoins from slipping on the chase.

205. The *Planer* is a block of hard wood having one smooth, level surface. This block is used to "plane down" the type form by laying it on the type, and tapping it lightly with the mallet or quoin key. This planing drives each individual type to its feet, which is absolutely necessary for good presswork.

FIGURE 123—A PLANER.

206. *Lock-Up Procedure*—Type forms are placed in the chase in such a manner that the longer dimensions of the paper upon which the form is printed is placed lengthwise on the press.

After the position of the form is determined and set in position in the chase, furniture is placed around the form, leaving space for quoins at the top and right-hand side. Care is taken to see that the furniture does not bind against itself, so that the form will receive all the pressure from the quoins.

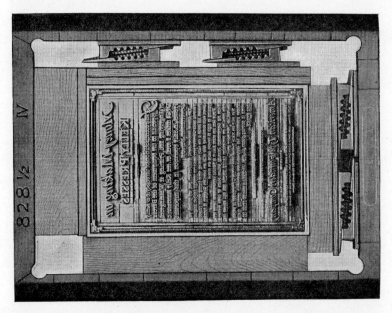

FIGURE 124—LOCKING A TYPE FORM IN A CHASE.

The proper arrangement of furniture around a form is shown in Figure 124. The quoins are tightened slightly with the fingers and the form is planed down. The quoins are serially tightened with the key, working toward the upper right corner of the chase. When moderate resistance is felt, the lock-up is tested by raising one corner of the chase and testing with the fingers. A properly justified form will "lift" (that is, each type will be held securely) if it is properly justified. If the quoins are of the "Hempel" make, shown in Figure 121, they must be placed so that the pressure of the wedge bears toward the furniture at the bottom and left, and not toward the quoins. This is pictured in Figure 124.

207. *Bearers* are strips of steel bent at right angles, often inserted in the ends of chases to insure the turning of press rollers to give an even distribution of ink.

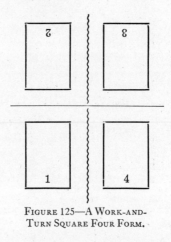

FIGURE 125—A WORK-AND-
TURN SQUARE FOUR FORM.

208. *Imposition* means the proper placing of page forms in a chase so that when locked up, printed and folded, each page is in its correct place. This term also includes the determining of the correct margins, registering the reverse forms, and the amount of trim of the complete book.

209. *Methods of Imposition*—There are two regular methods of imposing page forms, as follows:

1. Work-and-Turn Forms are those printed with the same form on both sides of the sheet. When cut in half and

folded, each piece makes one complete copy. For this reason, work-and-turn forms reduce presswork one-half.

2. Sheetwise Forms are those that are "backed up" (that is, printed on the other side) by a different type form.

210. *Square Four Imposition*—Figure 125 illustrates the imposing of a work-and-turn form. After printing, the sheet

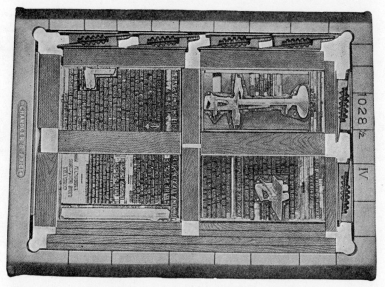

FIGURE 126—LOCKING UP A FOUR-PAGE FORM.

is turned end for end, and printed on the other side, so that page 1 backs up page 2, and page 4 backs up page 3. After cutting on the straight lines and folding on the wavy lines, as shown in the illustration, two sets of pages are formed, each numbering from 1 to 4, consecutively.

To print the same job sheetwise, pages 2 and 3 are printed on a sheet one-half this size, and backed up with pages 1 and 4.

211. *Long Four Imposition*—A work-and-turn long 4 page imposition is shown in Figure 127, which makes the same amount of consecutively numbered pages as the square four.

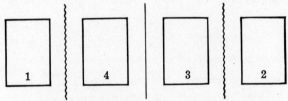

FIGURE 127—A WORK-AND-TURN LONG FOUR FORM.

In printing the long four sheetwise, the four pages on one side are printed first, and then backed up by turning the sheet end to end.

212. *The Square Eight Imposition*—Figure 128 represents a work-and-turn 8-page form. Two sections of 8 pages numbered consecutively, are obtained from this layout, when cut on the straight lines, and folded on the wavy lines.

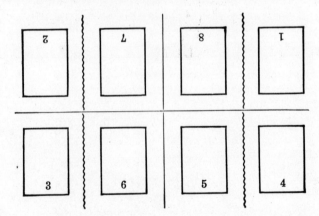

FIGURE 128—A WORK-AND-TURN 8-PAGE FORM.

213. *Twelve-Page Imposition*—Twelve pages, work-and-turn, are shown in Figure 129. This forms two sections after being backed-up and cut—one of 8 pages, and a smaller section of 4 pages.

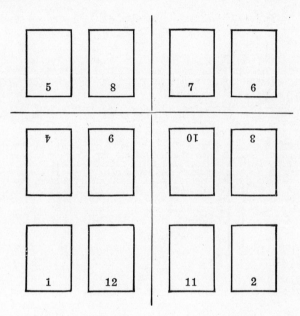

FIGURE 129—A WORK-AND-TURN 12-PAGE FORM.

214. *Sixteen-Page Imposition*—Figure 131 shows the method of arranging the page forms, work-and-turn, for a 16-page book. Printed sheetwise, the upper 8 pages form one section, and the bottom 8 the other.

215. *Signature Marks*—Books are usually printed in sections of 8-, 16-, 32- or 64-page sections. Each section of a book is called a "signature," and is marked in the gutter of the outside fold so that the binder can tell at a glance if the

sections are gathered properly.   Page numbers are referred
to as "folios."

12 by 18 inches	4 by 6 inches
9 by 12 inches	$3\frac{5}{8}$ by $5\frac{1}{8}$ inches
$5\frac{1}{8}$ by $7\frac{2}{3}$ inches	$3\frac{1}{8}$ by $4\frac{3}{4}$ inches
6 by 9 inches	3 by $4\frac{1}{2}$ inches
$4\frac{1}{2}$ by $6\frac{3}{4}$ inches	$2\frac{1}{2}$ by $3\frac{7}{8}$ inches

FIGURE 130—STANDARD UNTRIMMED BOOK SIZES.

216. *Book Trimming*—Three sides—the top, right side
and bottom—of a book must be trimmed so that the book will
be smooth, and the folded sheets cut so that they will open
properly. Allowance for this trim must be made in imposing
the book pages. One-quarter inch is usually a sufficient allowance for trim.

QUESTIONS FOR CLASS DISCUSSION

1. What equipment is necessary for locking up type forms? 201 to 205.

2. Of what purpose is the planer? 205.

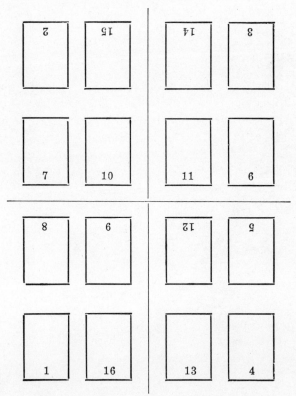

FIGURE 131—A WORK-AND-TURN 16-PAGE FORM.

3. Explain the locking-up procedure. 206.

4. What do you understand by the term "imposition"? 208.

5. What is a "work-and-turn" form?   209.

6. What is meant by a "sheetwise" form?   210.

7. How does book trimming effect the imposition of the type forms?   216.

8. What is a "signature"? A "folio"?   215.

BOOKS FOR FURTHER READING

REED, "Science of Imposition," Inland Printer Co.

I. T. U. LESSONS, Unit 7, Lessons 3 to 10.

U. T. A. LESSONS, Vols. 24 to 25.

CHAPTER XIII

PRINTING PRESSES

217. *Kinds of Printing Presses*—There are three kinds of printing presses: the platen, the cylinder, and the rotary.

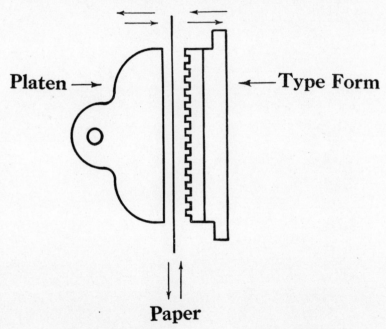

FIGURE 132—DIAGRAMMATIC VIEW OF A PLATEN PRESS.

218. *The Platen Press*—There are two kinds of platen presses: the "sliding platen," or "rigid bed," in which the platen is placed parallel with the bed and then drawn up against it; and the "clam-shell" press, in which the platen rocks up against the bed, and the bed advances to meet it. A clam-shell press is shown in Figure 133, and the sliding platen in Figure 134.

Platen presses range in size from 5 by 8 inches to $14\frac{1}{2}$ by 22 inches. Special sizes for certain kinds of work often run larger.

219. *Parts of the Platen Press*—The parts of the platen press are illustrated in Figure 133. The rollers receive their

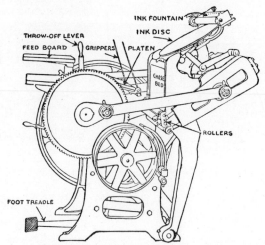

FIGURE 133—PARTS OF A PLATEN PRESS.

supply of ink from the disc, and pass twice over the form for each impression. The fountain is used to feed small amounts of ink regularly to the top roller at each print. The sheets of paper are placed on the platen. The grippers hold the sheet of paper fast to the platen after the impression is made. When the throw-off lever is in the upper position, the type form fails to print on the paper in the press. When the lever is forward, the platen receives the impression.

220. *Printing Rollers*—The ink rollers of the printing press are made of glue, glycerine and molasses, and other substances in small quantities.

The rollers should never be left standing on the type form of ink disc. If this is done, the rollers will carry an impression of the type, or a flat surface where they rested against the plate. The rollers should be placed in the lowest position when the press is not in operation.

221. *Inking the Platen Press*— The platen press should be inked before the form is put into place on the bed. This procedure will prevent large, heavy spots of ink from adhering to the type. During the press run, inking must be done by placing a very small quantity near the edge of the disc

FIGURE 134—A THOMPSON PRESS OF THE SLIDING PLATEN GROUP.

where it revolves upward. In this way the ink spots are partially distributed before they find their way to the form.

222. *Platen Press Make-Ready*—The term "make-ready" applies to preparing the press for a job. Two "tympan sheets" are cut, as shown in Figure 135, and placed on the platen, held firmly by the bales. Two or three sheets of pressboard are then placed under the tympan. Several "sheets," made up of news or book paper, are added above the pressboard.

After this procedure, the chase containing the type form is placed in the press, in the proper position, quoins up, against the bed. The grippers must be immediately adjusted so that they will clear the form when the first impression is made. Should the form strike the gripper, it will be smashed.

An impression is then made on the tympan. If the impression is not clear, more pressboard is needed; if too much impression is made, a sheet or more of pressboard must be removed.

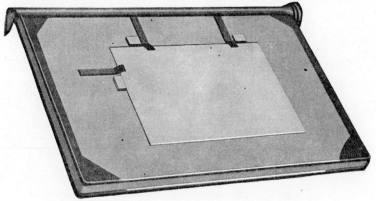

FIGURE 135—THE USE OF QUAD GUIDES AND PAPER FENDERS.

223. *"Guides"* for the sheets were formerly made by pasting 3-em 12-point quads to the tympan. Fenders are made of stiff cardboard and pasted next the quads to prevent the sheets from slipping over the quads while printing. Quad guides are shown mounted on a tympan in Figure 135. "Gauge-pin" guides are more popular than quads because they can be more readily adjusted. Pins are shown in Figure 136.

To locate the guides, the pressman measures from the edges of the impression on the tympan, and then draws lines outlining the sheet. The bottom guides should be set about an inch from each corner of the sheet, and the side guide slightly below the center of the sheet. Care must be taken to see that the grippers do not strike the guides, but in the margins of the sheet. If the margins are too small, a string is stretched between the grippers in such a way that the paper is held fast to the tympan.

When the first printed sheet is examined, it may be found that part of the form is printing badly. This is caused by

FIGURE 136—THE USE OF GAUGE PIN GUIDES.

worn type, and the fact that the solid sections of the form require more impression. To remedy this fault, the form may be "underlayed," "overlayed," or "interlayed."

224. The *Underlay* is used usually behind engravings and blocks. A piece of paper or cardboard is placed behind the form in order to bring that section to the correct height. Underlays are usually resorted to when part of the form is so low that it receives an insufficient supply of ink from the rollers.

225. An *Overlay* consists of paper pasted to the tympan undersheet to give more impression to the parts of the form that do not print properly. In order to place this overlay properly, an impression is made on the undersheet. This is done by releasing the top tympan sheet from the lower bale, holding the upper end out of the press, and operating the machine so that the print is taken. Then the top sheet is replaced.

226. *Interlays* consist of sheets of paper or cardboard placed between the engravings or electrotypes and the wooden bases upon which they are nailed.

227. *Chalk Overlays*—A quickly made relief overlay, suitable for the printing of halftone engravings and Ben Day etchings, is made by a patented process. A special sheet is printed in the press, using a patented ink, and etched in a simple chlorinated lime solution. This sheet is then placed under the tympan on the press.

228. *Hand-Feeding the Platen Press*—The process of printing sheets in a press is called "press-feeding." The sheets are fed against the guides with the right hand. The printed sheet is removed by the left hand simultaneously with the feeding of the blank sheet, and piled directly in front of the operator. The press-feeder times his movements with those of the press, and as many as 1,400 sheets an hour may be printed. Care must be taken to see that the fingers of the left hand do not touch the fresh ink, as this will smear it.

To facilitate feeding, the sheets may be "fanned out" by rubbing the thumb nail over the pile so that the sheets will project slightly over each other.

The throw-off lever is always thrust swiftly back should a sheet be fed in crookedly, or when a sheet is missed. If an impression is made on the tympan, it must be washed off with machine oil and a clean rag.

229. *Washing the Platen Press*—After the type has been removed from the press and thoroughly cleaned with gasoline and a stiff brush, the press must be cleaned. This is done by distributing kerosene on the ink disc when the rollers are brought up to the top of the bed. Then the disc is washed off with a soiled rag. The rollers are wiped in turn, finishing with the top roller. The plate and rollers are then gone over with a clean rag, so that no trace is left of the printing ink.

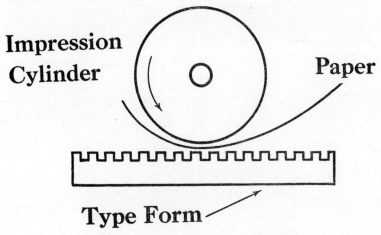

FIGURE 137—DIAGRAMMATIC VIEW OF THE CYLINDER PRESS.

230. *Cylinder Presses*—The cylinder press prints by means of a cylinder which rolls against the type form. The printed sheets are delivered automatically. Only a small part of the form receives the impression at one time, as shown in Figure 137, which illustrates the principle of the cylinder press.

231. *Styles of Cylinder Presses*—There are four styles of cylinder presses: the drum cylinder, the two-revolution, the stop cylinder, and the perfecting cylinder.

232. *The Drum Cylinder* makes one revolution when printing a sheet of paper. Only one-half of the cylinder is used for making the impression, the other part being cut

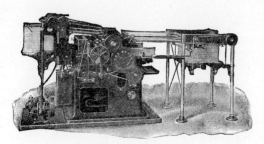

FIGURE 138—A KELLY TWO-REVOLUTION CYLINDER PRESS. WITH FEEDER.

down. The bed of the press, on which the type form is placed, moves forward and backward with each revolution of the press.

FIGURE 139—A LEE TWO-REVOLUTION CYLINDER PRESS.

233. *The Two-Revolution Cylinder Press*—The cylinder of the two-revolution cylinder press prints the paper while making one revolution, and is lifted clear of the form during the second revolution. The impression cylinder of this press is only one-half as large as that of the drum cylinder. The two-revolution is the most used in printing establishments. Two popular models are shown in Figures 138 and 139.

234. *The Stop-Cylinder Press*—The cylinder of the stop-cylinder press stops after making an impression and remains stationary during the return of the type form.

235. *Perfecting Presses* print on both sides of the web or sheet at one time, fold, and often paste in one operation.

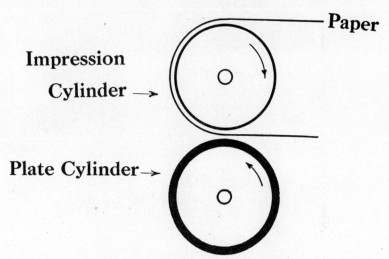

Impression
Cylinder →

Plate Cylinder →

Paper

FIGURE 140—DIAGRAMMATIC VIEW OF A ROTARY PRESS.

236. *Rotary (Web) Presses* print from curved printing plates. The paper is usually automatically fed in single sheets, or run from a roll through the machine. The paper passes between the printing plate and the impression cylinder as shown in Figure 140. The paper from the roll is called a "web," which is printed on both sides, folded into complete signatures of a book or magazine, or into a complete newspaper. One method of attaching curved plates to a cylinder on large newspaper presses is shown in Figure 141. Figure 142 illustrates a sheet-fed rotary press capable of printing 7,500 sheets per hour.

237. *Rotary Newspaper Presses* consist of "units," each one of which prints a certain number of pages of the complete newspaper. These units usually extend in a straight line, and

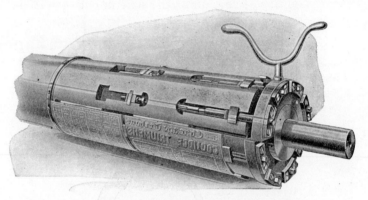

FIGURE 141—ONE METHOD OF MOUNTING CURVED STEREOTYPES ON THE PLATE CYLINDER OF A NEWSPAPER ROTARY PRESS.

in large plants often 160 feet in length, and two stories in height.

Great speeds are attained by these mammoth newspaper presses. Some print 420,000 papers an hour up to 12 pages; 336,000 an hour of 14 or 16 pages; 210,000 an hour of 18, 22 or 24 pages; 168,000 an hour of 26, 28, 30 or 32 pages; 126,000 an hour from 34 to 40 pages; 105,000 an hour from 44 to 48 pages; and 84,000 an hour of 52, 56, or 64 pages. These presses not only print, but automatically fold, count and deliver the finished newspaper to the mailing room of the plant. Figure 143 illustrates one of the smaller sizes of newspaper presses.

238. *Automatically Fed Presses,* it is estimated, will print 100 per cent more sheets than those fed by the hand method. Automatically fed cylinder and platen presses turn out as many as 3500 sheets per hour. On some makes of platen feeders attachments may be had that allow the feeding of

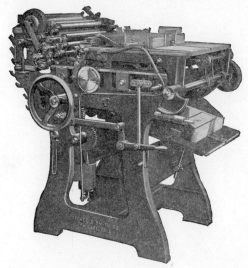

FIGURE 142—A STOKES & SMITH SHEET-FED ROTARY PRESS.

two small cards, blotters or envelopes at one time. An automatically fed cylinder press is shown in Figure 138. Very short runs are more economically fed by hand.

238a. *Non-Offset Guns*—These machines have been developed for the prevention of "offset," that is, the smudging and sticking of ink on a printed sheet to the one following it in the pile, as they come from the press.

A mixture of starch dextrine, alcohol, and water, and other liquids in smaller amounts, is sprayed by the action of

FIGURE 143—A GOSS ROTARY NEWSPAPER PRESS.

compressed air onto each sheet as it leaves the delivery end of automatically-fed printing presses.

With these devices, it is possible to eliminate offset, and make possible the "backing up" of sheets almost immediately after printing. The fine coating on the sheets is invisible, and

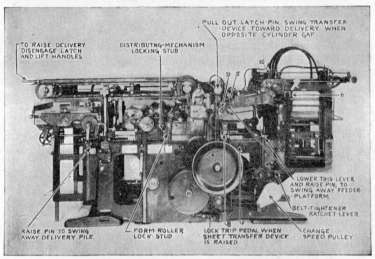

FIGURE 144a—A MIEHLE HORIZONTAL CYLINDER PRESS.

can be detected only by running the fingers lightly over the printed sheet. No difficulties are found in the printing of color work.

QUESTIONS FOR CLASS DISCUSSION

1. Name three kinds of printing presses, and explain the operation of each.   217, 218, 230, 236.

2. Be able to point out the parts of the platen press.   219.

3. Of what substances are printing rollers made?   220.

4. What two things must be remembered on the care of printing rollers?   220.

5. How should the platen press be inked?   221.

6. What is meant by "make ready"?   222.

7. What are "tympan sheets"? "Slipsheets"?   222.

8. Explain the use of "guides."   223.

9. What is meant by "underlay," "overlay," and "interlay"? 224, 225, 226.

10. Explain the operation of "pressfeeding."   228.

11. How should the press be washed?   229.

12. Name the four styles of cylinder presses, and tell the principle of each.   231 to 235.

13. How does the rotary press operate?   236.

14. Discuss the speeds of newspaper presses.   237.

15. Explain the advantages of automatic pressfeeding.   238.

16. Explain the function of a non-offset gun.   238a.

BOOKS FOR FURTHER READING

SPICHER, "The Practice of Presswork."

ST. JOHN, "Practical Hints on Presswork, Inland Printer Co.

—— "Rotary-Web Presswork," Inland Printer Co.

THOMAS, "Concise Manual of Platen Presswork," Inland Printer Co.

FIGURE 144*b*—A MIEHLE VERTICAL CYLINDER PRESS.

CHAPTER XIV

PRINTING PLATES

239. The term "photo-engraving" means the making of printing plates by the chemical action of light on a film. The following kinds of printing plates are made by the photo-engraving method: line etchings, halftones, and color process plates taken through color filters from full color copy.

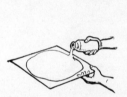

FIGURE 145—COATING THE GLASS WITH ALBUMEN.

FIGURE 146—DIPPING THE PLATE IN A SILVER BATH.

FIGURE 147—PHOTOGRAPHING THE COPY.

240. *Line Etchings* duplicate only black and white, and may be made from pen and ink drawings, sketches, plans, hand-lettering, and proofs of type forms. Line etchings are made by the following process:

(a) Making the Negative—A "wet" plate is prepared in the following manner: A piece of plate glass is covered with albumen (white of egg and water) and coated with collodion and allowed to dry. The plate is then made sensitive to light by dipping it into a vat of silver nitrate. The sensitized plate

147

is placed in a holder, which in turn is placed on the camera. Negatives are also made on dry plates and film and developed in the usual manner as snapshots. A process camera must be used, however. The camera lens is then uncapped, and an

FIGURE 148—DEVELOP-
ING THE PLATE.

FIGURE 149—STRIP-
PING THE NEGATIVE
FILM.

FIGURE 150—SCRUB-
BING THE ZINC PLATE
WITH POWDERED PUM-
ICE.

exposure of the copy is made on the sensitized plate. After developing, the plate becomes a "negative." The negative is now stripped from the glass, and mounted upon a strip of one-quarter inch plate glass.

FIGURE 151—PRINTING
THROUGH THE NEGATIVE
ON THE ZINC PLATE.

FIGURE 152—INKING
THE ZINC PLATE.

FIGURE 153—POW-
DERING THE ZINC
PLATE WITH DRAGON'S
BLOOD.

(b) Making the Print—The zinc plate, which will be etched so that it will duplicate the copy, is prepared by coating with albumen, water, and bichromate of ammonia. The negative and zinc plate are put in close contact, and exposed to a strong light. The plate is now a photographic print on

PRINTING PLATES 149

zinc. The print is rolled with specially prepared ink, and placed under running water and rubbed with a piece of cotton. Wherever the negative is transparent, the light made a coating on the zinc, and this remains as the picture. The rest of the coating is washed off, leaving the bare zinc exposed. Prints are also made with cold top enamel, which are developed in a special alcoholic bath and washed with water; from this point the same procedure takes place as above.

FIGURE 154—A ZINC ETCHING MACHINE.

(c) Dragon's Blood—The zinc plate is now dusted over with a red powder called "dragon's blood," which adheres to the inked parts of the plate. The plate is heated so that the dragon's blood forms an acid-proof coating over all the lines in the picture.

(d) Etching—The zinc is immersed in a solution of nitric acid and water in the etching machine. The action of the acid

FIGURE 155—A HALFTONE SCREEN.

etches away that part of the plate which is unprotected by the dragon's blood, that is, the surface of the plate which will not form a part of the picture. This process of dusting and etching is continued until the plate is deeply etched. Then the acid-proof is washed off with hot lye.

(e) Finishing—The high portions of the non-printing surfaces of the plate are then routed away, and hand-tooled to assure perfection. The plate is nailed to a wood block, to make it type high, which is the finishing operation.

241. The *Halftone* differs from the line etching in that it reproduces "half tones," that is, the intermediate gray shades in the copy. Halftones may be made from photographs, wash drawings, water-color and oil paintings, and the natural object. Almost anything that can be photographed can be duplicated on a printing plate by the halftone process, which follows:

(a) The Screen—The halftone plate is prepared similarly to that of the line etching. The photographing is done, how-

  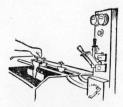

FIGURE 156 — PHOTO-
GRAPHING THROUGH THE
HALFTONE SCREEN.

FIGURE 157—PRINTING
THROUGH THE NEGATIVE
ON THE COPPER PLATE.

FIGURE 158—AN
ELECTRIC ETCHING
MACHINE.

ever, through a "halftone screen." This screen consists of two pieces of glass, each having opaque parallel lines engraved diagonally upon it. The pieces are cemented together so that the lines cross each other at right angles, forming a screen. The number of lines to the inch determines the screen, which number from 50 to 175. This screen is placed in the camera, and the photograph is broken up into a series of infinitesimal dots before reaching the wet plate. The negative is made as in making the line etching, and a copper plate is specially prepared to receive the photograph. The copy is transferred from the negative to the copper plate in the printing frame.

(b) Preparing the Copper Plate—The copper plate is washed, and the coating between the dots is thereby removed. The plate is then soaked in violet aniline dye, which colors each dot. After "burning in" over a gas flame, the coating on the dots turns into an acid-proof enamel.

(c) Etching the Halftone—The copper halftone plate is now placed in an electric etching machine, which dissolves

FIGURE 159—A 65-LINE SCREEN HALFTONE.

FIGURE 160—A 150-LINE SCREEN HALFTONE.

the exposed copper between each dot. After re-etching and hand-tooling, the finished plate is nailed to a block to make it type high. The halftone gives the most faithful reproduction of a continuous tone picture.

242. The *Halftone Screen*—On a 65-line screen halftone, shown in Figure 159, there are 65 parallel lines to the inch each way, making 4,225 dots to the square inch. Finer screens have accordingly smaller dots. Figure 160 shows a 150-line screen, and Figure 161 a 133-line screen.

In Figure 162 is shown an enlargement of a section of Figure 161. It has been enlarged eight times. If it is held at a slight distance and the eyes squinted slightly, the resemblance to the marked-off section in Figure 161 will then be noted. This enlargement points out how, in the darker parts of the picture, the black dots almost come together, and in

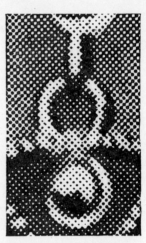

FIGURE 161—A 133-LINE SCREEN HALFTONE. (NOTE THE MARKED-OFF SECTION WHICH IS ENLARGED IN FIG. 162.)

FIGURE 162—AN ENLARGED SECTION OF FIGURE 161, SHOWING SMALL DOTS THAT MAKE UP THE HALFTONE.

the black parts of the picture, they do converge. In the light parts of the picture, the dots are farther apart.

Halftone Screen Suited to Paper Stock—The 50- to 65-line screen is used mostly for newspaper work, and in printing on rough paper stocks. The 85- to 100-line screens, however, can be used on newspapers that do not stereotype the pages for printing. The 100- to 133-line screens are suited to machine finish and English finish book paper. Screens over 133-line are printed on enameled stock. See the table below for a suitable screen guide.

HALFTONE SCREEN GUIDE

News stock...................................... 50 to 85 screen
Bond, ledger, linen cover......................... 85 to 100 screen
Machine finish book, s. & s. c.................... 100 to 133 screen
Dull finish coated book........................... 120 to 150 screen
Enameled stocks................................. 150 to 175 screen

A fine screen halftone can not be used on rough paper stock because the dots would be forced into the fibers of the paper. This would in turn force ink into the space between the dots, filling in the open spaces with ink, and resulting in "dirty" printing.

243. *Ordering Engravings*—Great care should be taken in ordering engravings to avoid delays and remake-up of type matter necessary when plates are ordered "off-size."

Directions to the photo-engraver should be written on a piece of paper and tipped onto the margin of the photograph —not fastened with a paper clip. The clip often cracks the copy and appears in the finished plate. See Figure 163*a*. Do not write on the back of a photograph—it will often appear in the halftone, as shown in Figure 163*b*.

Do not mark on the photo to designate the size, as the engraver must make the plate smaller, and make the copy worthless for further use. See Figure 164*a*. The correct way to show the "crop marks" is shown in Figure 165*b*, where the photograph is pasted onto a larger sheet of paper or cardboard.

It is better never to roll a picture, as cracks may appear, as shown in Figure 165*a*.

Scaling Copy—To find the height of the engraving from a known width of any photograph, place a sheet of tissue over the photograph, and draw a diagonal line, taking care not to indent the photograph. From this diagonal, the cor-

FIGURE 163a—RESULT OF USING A PAPER CLIP ON A PHOTOGRAPH.

FIGURE 163b—RESULT OF WRITING ON THE BACK OF A PHOTOGRAPH.

FIGURE 164a—THE WRONG WAY TO MARK A PHOTOGRAPH FOR SIZE.

FIGURE 164b—THE CORRECT WAY TO MARK A PHOTOGRAPH FOR SIZE.

FIGURE 165a—RESULT OF ROLLING A PHOTOGRAPH.

FIGURE 165b—FINDING THE CORRECT HEIGHT FROM A KNOWN WIDTH.

Plates Courtesy of American Photo-Engravers Association.

rect height can be determined for the plate wanted, as shown
in Figure 165*b*.

Care of Plates—Engravings should be carefully brushed
with gasoline after using, and then wrapped in heavy paper,
allowing several thicknesses over the face of the engraving.

244. *Ben Day Screens and Other Shading Mediums*—The
Ben Day Process and shading mediums are a mechanical
method of producing a shaded background or other tonal
values in a zinc plate. Combinations of shading mediums can

FIGURE 166—A LINE ETCHING SHOWING THE
USE OF BEN DAY SCREENS.

also be used for color on black and white halftones. As many
colors may be used as desired, each color to be printed one
above the other, a black plate being the last. This shading
or printing may be done in a great variety of line, grain, and
stipple, and other patterns. A transparent film is inked and
placed faced down on the picture, plate, or negative. With
a burnisher, the operator offsets the shading on certain parts
of the subject. Figure 166 illustrates a line etching improved
by the Ben Day Process.

245. *Wood Engravings*—Before the invention of photography, the hand-cut wood block was used exclusively for illustrating purposes. Now the wood block is used for the illustration of jewelry and other work.

Wood engravings are usually cut from boxwood, which is hard and has a close grain. The copy is either drawn, traced, or photographed directly upon the wood block. The engraving is usually done by hand, although the broader surfaces are cut with a special ruling machine. Figure 167 is printed from a wood block.

FIGURE 167—A WOOD BLOCK.

246. *Linoleum Blocks*—The simplest form of illustrating is by printing from linoleum blocks. The design is either drawn directly on the linoleum, or is transferred with ordinary carbon paper. The piece of linoleum is glued fast to a wooden base to bring it to type height. The parts not intended to print are cut out very easily with an ordinary pocket knife, or a gouge. For fine work, however, a special V-shaped engraving tool is best.

HALFTONES FROM COLORED COPY

Blue reproduces almost white.
White reproduces light gray.
Gray reproduces light gray.
Purple reproduces medium gray.
Bright green reproduces dark gray.
Brown reproduces almost black.
Black reproduces black.

246a. *Rubber Plate Printing* is done from both molded and hand-cut rubber blocks. Much of this work is done by hand from plates mounted on a wood base to type height.

Rubber blocks have the faculty of making a much better impression than does linoleum, which often leaves a rough, gray impression on the paper.

In cutting rubber plates, a design or lettering is either drawn on or transferred to the printing surface of the block, and the lines cut down to the fabric between the rubber printing surface and the block. After the design is cut out, pliers are used to strip out that material in which the "white space" will appear on the printed work. On other types of rubber plates, the design is gouged out in relief the same as in cutting a linoleum block.

QUESTIONS FOR CLASS DISCUSSION

1. What does the term "photoengraving" mean?   239.

2. Differentiate between the line etching and the halftone. 240, 241.

3. Briefly explain the making of a line plate.   240.

4. Briefly explain the making of a halftone.   241.

5. What halftone screens should be used on news stock?   242.

6. If you were sending engravings to a stereotyped newspaper, what screen would you provide?   242.

7. What screen should be used in printing a book of this type?   242.

8. What screens are suitable for fine, glossy, enameled stocks? 242.

9. Explain the Ben Day Process.   244.

10. What kind of illustrations are sometimes engraved on wood? Why?   245.

11. What is the simplest form of illustrating?   How is it done? 246.

12. What advantage has rubber plate printing over linoleum? 246a.

13. What mistakes should one be careful of in ordering engravings?   243.

14. How is copy scaled?   243.
15. How should plates be stored?   243.

BOOKS FOR FURTHER READING

AMERICAN PHOTO-ENGRAVERS ASSOCIATION—"Achievement in Photo-Engraving and Printing, 1927."

GRESS—"Handbook of Printing."

HACKLEMAN—"Commercial Engraving and Printing."

HORGAN—"Photo-Engraving Primer," Inland Printer Co.

POLK—"Essentials of Linoleum Block Printing," Manual Arts Press.

Chapter XV

DUPLICATE PRINTING PLATES

247. *Duplicate Printing Plates* may be made by two processes: electrotyping and stereotyping. The advantages of duplicate plates are listed below:

1. To save the originals for future runs. This enables the printer to distribute the original forms. Expensive engravings are usually saved and duplicates of the originals sent to the presses. Wear would soon necessitate the making of new plates if the originals were used.

2. To save wear on expensive and delicate types.

3. To print in gangs.

4. To allow the same set-up to be printed at the same time in several different locations.

248. *Electrotypes* are copper- or nickel-faced duplicates of type forms or engravings. The electrotyping process is explained as follows:

(a) Molding—A wax plate or sheet lead is prepared, then dusted with graphite to prevent sticking. The subject to be electrotyped is pressed or "molded" into the wax. When the wax has "set" under great pressure it is known as a "mold."

(b) Preparing the Mold—The mold is trimmed even, and all open spaces are raised or "built up" by hand. The graphited plate is then washed, and all parts not to be used are "blocked out" with wax.

159

(c) Electroplating—An electrical connection is now made with the graphited mold. To speed electroplating, the mold

FIGURE 168—AN ELECTROTYPE MOLDING PRESS.

FIGURE 169—A WAX MOLD.

is given a thin coating of copper solution. The mold is then placed in an electroplating bath which covers the graphited

FIGURE 170—PLACING THE MOLD IN AN ELECTROPLATING BATH.

FIGURE 171—THE BACK OF THE ELECTROTYPE SHELL.

surfaces with a thin coating of copper. Electrotypes are also made of nickel.

(d) Backing the Shell—When the mold is removed from the bath, the wax is melted from the copper shell which was deposited by the electroplating process. The shell is next cleaned, and the back is covered with tin foil. Heating fuses the two together. Molten metal is now poured over the back of the shell, which adheres to the tin foil. The result is the "cast," or plate, which is planed about three-sixteenths of an

FIGURE 172—POURING METAL INTO THE BACK OF THE ELECTROTYPE SHELL.

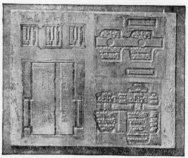

FIGURE 173—AN ELECTROTYPE CAST.

inch thick. After all defects are removed, the electrotype is usually mounted on wood to type height, or shaved to 11 points for patent base, or curved for rotary purposes.

249. *Nickel-Steel Electrotypes* are made with a coating of nickel steel. These plates are more durable than copper, and also withstand the destroying chemicals of certain inks.

250. *Correcting Bad Forms in Electrotyping*—Bad type forms, as those having border corner breaks, low type, etc., may be corrected in the plate by the electrotyper. In having a plate made for several colors, there is no need for the compositor to set each color form separately. The electrotyper makes a whole plate for each color, and routs from each plate all but the color wanted.

251. *Mounting Electrotypes*—A modern method of mounting plates type high is in the use of "patent base," or blocks. Plates to be used in this way are planed to 11-point thickness (.153-inch), and usually beveled on the edges. The elec-

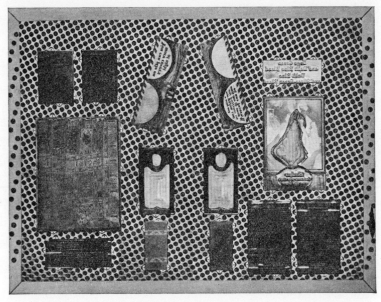

FIGURE 174*a*—"HONEYCOMB" PATENT BASE WITH PLATES MOUNTED
BY REGISTER HOOKS.

trotypes or other plates are held to the blocks by small "register hooks," as shown in Figures 174*a* to 174*c*.

Advantages of metal base over wood are many—saving in the first cost of the plates, increased life of the plates, fifty per cent makeready and register time saved, absolute hairline register of color plates, rigidity against impression, no "working up" of material in the form, and the ability to handle all sizes and shapes of plates.

Bases are made in four styles: "honeycomb," "diagonal," "sectional," and special "book blocks." Some base material is made in four-inch square sections, with filling pieces of various sizes to allow for locking in the various sized chases.

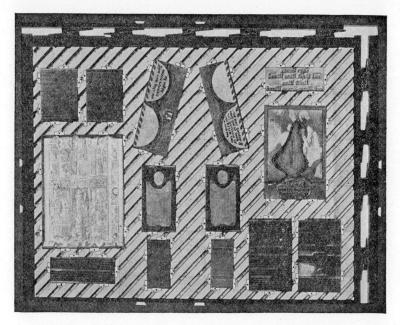

FIGURE 174b—"DIAGONAL" PATENT BASE WITH PLATES MOUNTED
BY REGISTER HOOKS.

They are made of malleable iron, cast iron, aluminum alloy, or semi-steel.

252. *Stereotyping*—A "stereotype" is a duplicate printing plate cast from a paper matrix. Stereotypes are used chiefly by newspapers and some book printers. Features, advertising illustrations, and news pictures are usually sent in matrix form to newspapers subscribing to news syndicates.

Stereotypes are coarse, as compared to electrotypes, and are not capable of showing the same fine detail, nor do they hold up for as many impressions on the press. Stereotypes may be plated with perhaps copper or chromium, in which case they are much more durable than the regular metal cast.

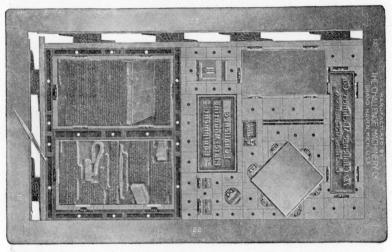

FIGURE 174c—"SECTIONAL" PATENT BASE WITH PLATES MOUNTED BY REGISTER HOOKS.

Because of the cheapness and quick method of making, stereotypes are well adapted to newspaper work. Stereotypes are made by the following two methods:

(a) The form or engraving is locked in a chase and taken to a "stereotyping press," as shown in Figure 175.

(b) The Dry Stereotyping Method—A matrix, or "flong," which is made of a heavy, prepared paper, is placed over the form in the stereotype press. The matrix, in turn, is covered with a molding blanket, and the form is then subjected to great pressure beneath the roller of the press. This action makes a clear, deep impression of the type form on the matrix.

(c) The Wet Stereotyping Method—The matrix is prepared in wet form. This wet matrix is laid over the form and either beaten with wire brushes or rolled in a matrix press. The matrix is then dried with steam.

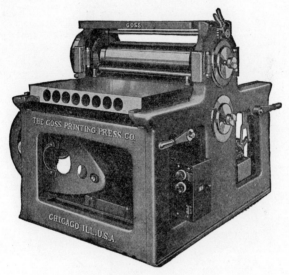

FIGURE 175—A MATRIX PRESS.

(d) When the matrix has been prepared, it is trimmed and placed in a "casting box," as pictured in Figure 176. Stereotype metal (which is softer than type metal) is poured into the box, and a duplicate form is cast from the matrix.

(e) When cooled, the matrix is next stripped from the duplicate plate, or stereotype. The duplicate is then planed type high, or, if cast in "shell" form, is mounted on wood or patent stereotype base.

253. *Curved Stereotypes*, in half-cylinder form, are made in the method explained above to fit the cylinders in large high-speed rotary newspaper presses.

254. *Wax Engraving*—Wax engraving is a common method of making maps, rule forms, and the like. The copy

FIGURE 176—A STEREOTYPE CASTING BOX.

is drawn or photographed directly upon a wax-covered metal plate. The work is engraved by sharp tools, much like the cutting of wood blocks. Both straight lines and curves are cut by special ruling machines. The procedure of casting the plate is the same as in making electrotypes.

An electrotype of a type form will show signs of wear after printing 40,000 impressions.

A lead mold nickeltype will show signs of wear after printing over 300,000 impressions.

A nickel-faced copper electrotype will show signs of wear after printing 200,000 impressions.

A chromium-plated electrotype will show signs of wear after printing over 700,000 impressions.

A stereotype shows signs of wear after printing 25,000 impressions.

FIGURE 177—DURABILITY OF PRINTING PLATES.

QUESTIONS FOR CLASS DISCUSSION

1. Name four advantages of duplicate plates.   247.

2. Briefly explain how electrotypes are made.   248.

3. What advantage do you see in mounting electrotypes on a patent block base?   251.

4. From what are stereotypes cast?   How are stereotypes cast? 252.

5. What kind of duplicate printing plates will stand the most impressions? Which one will stand the least? Figure 177.

6. Explain wax engraving, and tell its purpose to the industry. 254.

BOOKS FOR FURTHER READING

HACKLEMAN, "Commercial Engraving and Printing."

HORGAN, "Photo-Engraving Primer," Inland Printer Co.

PARTRIDGE, "Electrotyping," Inland Printer Co.

SALADE, "Handbook of Electrotyping and Stereotyping," Inland Printer Co.

Chapter XVI

INK AND COLOR

255. *Printing Ink*, unlike writing ink, is of the same consistency as thick paint. This pasty form enables the composition rollers to carry the ink to the type forms or printing plates without dripping or smearing.

There are many kinds of printing ink manufactured for letterpress printing, lithographic printing and intaglio printing. Special inks in these groups are made to print upon different grades of paper stock. Some of these, for example, are bond ink, cover ink, halftone ink, and process ink. There are many others. Inks suitable to certain kinds of papers are shown in Figure 178.

Paper	Ink	Reducer	Drier
Blotting	Halftone, Book	Soft Halftone	Japan
Book, E. F.	Book	00 Varnish	Cobalt
Book, *Eggshell*	Book	00 Varnish	Cobalt
Book, *Antique*	Book	Halftone	Cobalt
Book, *Coated*	Halftone	Soft Halftone	Japan
Bond	Bond	Halftone	Cobalt
Bristol	Job, Book	Halftone	Cobalt
Cardboard	Job, Book	Halftone	Japan
Gummed, *Plain*	Book, Job	Halftone	Cobalt
Ledger	Bond	Job, Book	Cobalt
News	News, Book	00 Varnish	Japan
Poster	News, Book	00 Varnish	Japan

FIGURE 178—SUITING INKS, REDUCERS, AND DRIERS TO TYPES OF PAPER.

256. *Ingredients of Printing Ink*—Printing ink is made of two materials: the pigment, or color, and the medium, or varnish, which carries the pigment and causes it to adhere to the paper. These two materials are ground together very finely to produce the quality necessary to good printing ink. The most expensive inks are those finely ground.

257. *Pigments of Printing Ink*—The covering power, brilliancy and permanence are the most important properties of a pigment.

Color pigments are derived from three sources: mineral, vegetable, and animal. Some mineral pigments are: genuine ultramarine blue, yellow ochre, raw sienna, raw umber and Indian red. All of these are from imported earths. Through chemical action, artificial mineral pigments may be made in almost any color. In fact, most printing inks today are made from coal-tar pigments in a wide range of colors. A few vegetable pigments are: gamboge, a gum from a tree grown in Ceylon; indigo, from the leaves of the indigo plant; and yellow lake, from the quercitron bark. Some animal pigments are: sepia from the cuttle fish, and carmine from the cochineal insect.

Black pigments are made mostly from carbon black. Other sources are lampblack, or soot; ivory black and black minerals.

One pound of black book ink will cover 100 square inches on 1000 sheets.
One pound of blue will cover 90 square inches on 1000 sheets
One pound of red will cover 80 square inches on 1000 sheets.
One pound of yellow will cover 70 square inches on 1000 sheets.
One pound of white will cover 60 square inches on 1000 sheets.

FIGURE 179—ESTIMATING INK.

Rough stock requires two to three times the ink that smooth or coated stock requires. Five per cent is usually added to the cost if printing is done in black ink; 10 per cent if colored.

258. *The Medium of Printing Ink*—The medium, or varnish, of printing ink is of two classes: One which dries by oxidation, and one which is absorbed by the paper stock. The first is usually linseed oil, and the latter rosin oil. Gums and waxes are added to give greater consistency.

259. *Water-color Inks*—Printing with regular letterpress material from watercolor inks is possible with the use of either rubber printing rollers, or coating the composition rollers with a special solution.

Water colors are especially suited to all types of printing where unusual colors, bright shades, or dull, flat effects and soft tins are required. Other advantages of the use of water colors are that less offset is encountered, and quick drying with smoother laying qualities is obtained. Water-color printing is best suited to printing on rough finish paper.

In water-color printing all the constitutes of the ink are soluble or miscible in water. The vehicle of water-color inks are gums, glues, soaps, glycerine, syrups, alcohol, etc. The coloring matter is the same as in oil inks.

260. *Color Printing*—There are three primary colors: red, yellow and blue. By the proper mixing of these colors, any other color may be made. White and black are not considered as colors—white is light, and black is the absence of color.

By mixing any two of the primary colors, one of three secondary colors are made: green, orange, or purple. As seen in Figure 180, green is made by mixing yellow and blue; orange is made by mixing yellow and red, and purple is made by mixing red and blue.

By mixing any two of the secondary colors, three tertiary colors are made: citrine, russet, and olive. By consulting Figure 180 again, it is seen that citrine is made by mixing orange and green; russet is made by mixing orange and purple; and olive is made by mixing green and purple.

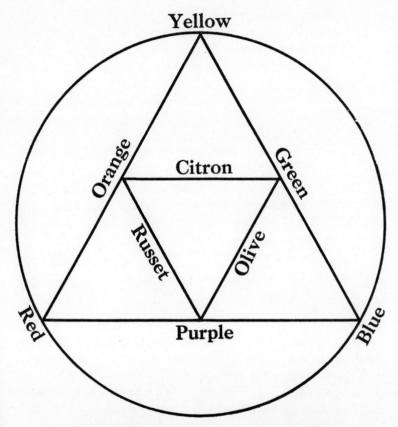

FIGURE 180—PRIMARY, SECONDARY AND TERTIARY COLORS.

261. *Hues*—Each color has many hues, which are obtained by varying the quantities used in mixing color. In this way we have different shades of color, as scarlet, scarlet red, and crimson red.

262. *Complementary Colors*—Complementary colors are those that neutralize each other when mixed, producing a neutral gray. Red and green, blue and orange, and yellow and purple are complementary colors. To soften or take away the intensity of red, its complementary, green, is added in small quantities. To soften green, a little red is added. Orange will soften blue, and yellow will soften purple, and vice versa.

Yellow....Nearest to light, and gives prominence to other colors. Yellow
          is used mostly for backgrounds.
Red......Lends heat and energy, and stands out and advances. Red is
          used for emphasis.
Blue......Blue is cold and retiring, and is not good for emphasis.
Green....Green is cool and restful to the eye.
Black.....Heavy black lends sobriety.

FIGURE 187—COLOR VALUES.

263. *Color Printing*—In printing color forms with line etchings and type, a separate form is required for each color. Line color plates are made in the same manner as one-color line etchings on zinc.

264. *Process Printing*—By the use of three transparent colors, red, yellow, and blue, illustrations may be printed that contain all the colors of the rainbow. This is accomplished by printing a yellow halftone plate first, the red next, and then blue. The various other hues and colors are made by the overlapping of these three primary colors.

The three primary colors cannot produce a good black, therefore a black plate is made, which is usually printed last. This black plate is the "key plate," and also strengthens the details of the picture. Figures 182 to 187 illustrate the various stages in printing with four-color process plates.

FIGURE 181—THE YELLOW PLATE.

FIGURE 182—THE RED PLATE.

FIGURE 183—THE RED PLATE PRINTED OVER THE YELLOW PLATE.

FIGURE 184—THE BLUE PLATE.

FIGURE 185—THE YELLOW, RED AND BLUE
PLATES COMBINED.

FIGURE 186—THE YELLOW, RED, BLUE
AND BLACK PLATES COMBINED.

Color of Paper	Color of Ink
Black..........	Dark red, gold and white, light blue, light blue and yellow brown.
Light blue......	Purple, dark blue, light yellow and yellow brown.
Dark blue......	Light blue and white, green and yellow red, dark red and gold.
Light brown....	Green, gray and lilac, dark brown and silver.
Dark brown.....	Light drab, yellow red, black and white.
Light green.....	Gold, dark brown, yellow red, dark green.
Dark red.......	Dark green, yellow red, dark blue, white and gold.
Light yellow....	Red, light blue.
White..........	Emerald green, navy green, crimson red.

FIGURE 188—GOOD COLOR COMBINATIONS.[1]

265. *Making Process Plates*—Four-color process plates are used in printing most of the magazine advertisements in color. The process plates may be made from either colored or black copy. The photographic plates are made with a color "filter" and a prism between the negative and the copy. Each filter absorbs certain colors, and allows others to photograph in full strength upon the negative. This process obtains the proper tone for each color.

265a. *Doping Ink*, that is, causing it to have more or less "tack" or drying qualities, is done by pressmen when they encounter difficulties in printing a job.

Varnishes are named from No. 00000 to No. 8, according to the various consistencies. No. 00000 to 0 is thin; 1 to 3 is medium, and 4 to 8 is heavy. Varnishes are made usually from the following oils: linseed, chinawood, tung, rosin, perilla, and various mineral oils. Varnishes are made to thin out, or "reduce," ink, and often to give it a glossy appearance.

Driers act as oxygen carriers and speed up the drying of ink. They are usually made from linoleate, resinate, tung-

[1] From Hackleman's "Commercial Engraving and Printing."

state of lead, borate and resinate of manganese, acetate and resinate of cobalt. Three kinds are used: *Paste*, which is used for slow drying; *Cobalt*, used for fast drying; and *Japan*, which is used on absorbent surfaces, having great penetrating qualities, and being quite volatile.

QUESTIONS FOR CLASS DISCUSSION

1. Name two ingredients of printing ink.   256.
2. Name two sources of black pigments.   257.
3. Name three sources of colored pigments.   257.
4. What advantages are claimed for water-color printing? 259.
5. What is the difference between water-color ink and oil ink? 259.
6. Name the three primary colors.   260.
7. Name the three secondary colors and tell how each is made. 260.
8. Name the three tertiary colors and tell how each is made. 260.
9. What is meant by a "complement"? Give two examples. 262.
10. Explain briefly how four-color process plates are made. 265.
11. How is four-color process printing done?   264.
12. What is a "color filter"?   265.
13. What is meant by "doping" ink?   265a.

BOOKS FOR FURTHER READING

HACKLEMAN, "Commercial Engraving and Printing," Pages 276 to 300; 575 to 590.

I. T. U. LESSONS, Job Unit 4, "Design and Color," Lesson 9.

INLAND PRINTER, "Modern Printing Inks."

LEHNER, "Ink Manufacture."

WIBORG, "Printing Ink."

Chapter XVII

COPPERPLATE ENGRAVING

266. Copperplate engraving is used for the more refined social and wedding accouncements, visiting cards, birth announcements, holiday greeting cards, and both business and social stationery. Copperplate engraving is unequaled in its dense black color and raised effect.

FIGURE 189—THE INTAGLIO PROCESS.

267. *Method of Engraving*—Copperplate engraving may be done either by hand or by machine. The engraving, or cutting, is done on a copper plate, usually. This cutting is called "intaglio," as the letters are cut into the printing plate, differing from "relief" printing which is done from "raised" letters, as from type.

268. *Copperplate Printing*—The engraved copper plate is mounted in an engraving press, several of which are shown and explained in Figure 190. Ink is rolled on the plate, which fills the cut-in lines of the engraving. The surface of the plate is then wiped, which takes off the ink from the surface of the plate, leaving, however, a good supply of ink in the cut-in sections. The paper is then pressed against the plate, and the ink leaves the cut-in portions of the plate and adheres to the paper or card. This process raises the ink above the surface of the paper, which can readily be seen or felt by rubbing a finger over the print. Color work is done in the same manner as in letterpress printing.

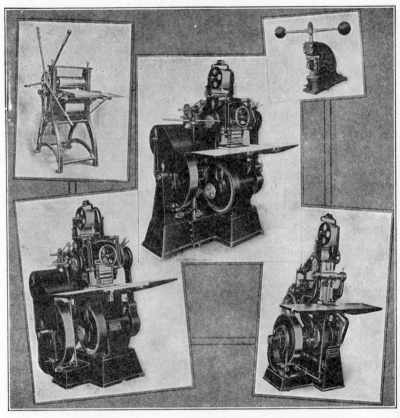

FIGURE 190—COPPERPLATE AND STEEL PLATE ENGRAVING PRESSES.

Copperplate engraving is slow and difficult, and is very expensive as compared with letterpress printing. The work is usually done by hand. Copperplate engraving is especially adapted to script lettering. The plates last only for a few hundred impressions before they are too badly worn to produce clear, sharp printing. Steel plates, being more durable, are used for long runs of notes and certificates.

269. *Thermography* is known as "raised letter" printing, and "process embossing." Thermography covers the process of printing with a slow-drying ink, over which powdered rosin is sprinkled. A heating process follows which fuses the

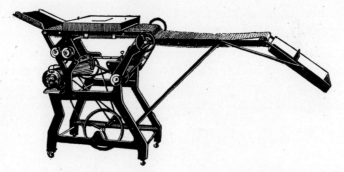

FIGURE 191—A VIRKOTYPE THERMOGRAPH MACHINE.

powder into the ink, and creates a raised surface on the printed letters. The printing is done with ordinary types. The sheets are dusted with powdered rosin usually by hand, and fed into the heating machine, one style of which is shown in Figure 191. Thermograph machines are procurable which take the sheets from an automatically fed press, dust them automatically with powder, heat and cool the finished sheets at a speed of over 2,000 sheets per hour.

270. *Embossing* is the process of stamping in relief either figures or characters on paper. A female die is etched intaglio in a zinc plate, and made type high. The plate is then locked up for the press from which the rollers have been removed. An impression is made from the die into a soft composition mounted on the platen of the press. After drying hard, this composition forms the male die. The sheets are fed into the press in the usual manner and are pressed between the two dies, which press or stamp the design or letters into the paper.

Paper is usually printed before being embossed, which makes the letters stand out from the paper. When the printing is eliminated, the process is called "blind embossing." The best embossing is done on specially built presses from electrically heated dies.

271. *Steel Rule Cutting*—Specialty printing, such as manufacturing labels, seals, and the like, are usually cut out after being printed and embossed. This cutting is done by bending steel rule to the required shape by hand or on special bending machines. The rule is then mounted into a wooden base, which strengthens and holds the rule into place. The cutting die is placed in a press in the usual manner, and fed as in embossing.

QUESTIONS FOR CLASS DISCUSSION

1. How can one determine genuine copperplate engraving? 266.
2. Explain briefly how copperplate engraving is done.   267.
3. How are the impressions made in copperplate engraving? 268.
4. What is meant by "thermography"?   269.
5. Explain the process of embossing.   270.
6. What is meant by the term "blind embossing"?   270.
7. How are odd-shaped printing jobs cut out?   271.

BOOKS FOR FURTHER READING

HACKLEMAN, "Commercial Engraving and Printing."
SALADE, "How to Make Cut-Outs," Oswald Publishing Co.
SALADE, "Plate Printing and Die Stamping," Inland Printer Co.

Chapter XVIII

LITHOGRAPHY, COLLOTYPE AND GRAVURE

272. *Lithography* was originated by Aloys Senefelder, a printer of music from copper plates in Munich, Germany, in 1798. At that time and until recently *calcareous* stones were used. A greasy medium was used for drawing designs and lettering upon the face of these stones. The affinity for grease on other parts of the stone was destroyed by applying a gum solution. The stone was dampened with a felt roller, and following that, inked by rollers. The moisture from the dampening rollers was absorbed by the

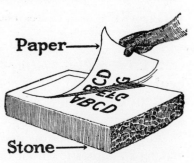

FIGURE 192—THE LITHOGRAPHIC PROCESS.

blank parts of the stone, and repelled by the inked parts. Conversely, the greasy ink used was repelled by the dampened parts of the stone, and clung to the greasy portions. Then the impression was made from the stone on the paper. Often the sheets were run fifteen times through the press to get the desired color effects. Figure 192 illustrates this process.

At present the old lithographic stone has been replaced, in most shops, by the aluminum or zinc plate, with a grained surface. These plates, which can be stretched around a cylin-

179

der, make possible the rotary press principle, with its great speeds.

273. *Offset Lithography*—Recently the offset lithography process came into being, in which the plate is mounted on a cylinder, and the designs and lettering are transferred to a second rubber-blanketed cylinder, from which the ink is transferred, or "offset," to the paper. See Figure 193 for a graphic explanation of offset lithography.

FIGURE 193—THE OFFSET LITHOGRAPHIC PROCESS.

274. *Offset Plate Making*—Offset plates can be prepared by three methods:

1. By drawing directly on the prepared metal plate, using a lithographic ink or greasy crayon.

2. By transferring the design or lettering to the plate by making an impression from the original plate with an especially prepared transfer paper, using transfer inks.

3. By applying the printed image on the offset plate by photographic methods, which is by far the most popular method used today.

The zinc plates are *grained* in a trough with marbles, special graining material, and water. After rotating for about an hour, the plate is sufficiently grained and is ready for further preparation.

The grained plates are then coated with albumen or fish glue in a *whirling machine,* and treated with ammonium bichromate, which hardens when exposed to light. The parts that are unexposed to light remain soluble in water.

The negative is put in contact with the plate in a *vacuum printing frame*, and arc lights make the exposure. The coating under the clear lines of the negative hardens, and is coated with a thin film of ink. A soaking in water removes the albumen from the unexposed parts of the plate.

Halftone Screens, usually from 60- to 150-line, can be placed in front of the negative in the camera to produce

FIGURE 194—A SHEET-FED HARRIS OFFSET PRESS.

tones, and colors can be separated by *filters* used with *panchromatic plates*. Science enters here in measuring the exposure by means of the photoelectric cell.

After *retouching*, the plate is ready for the press. The zinc or aluminum plate may be regrained after the run, and used again for another job.

Four kinds of negatives can be used in offset platemaking: The dry plate, the wet plate, the film, and the paper. Contact negatives can be made by photographing any printed job, such as office forms and letterheads, but photography only produces what has been printed—it cannot improve the work.

275. *Offset Lithography Presswork*—After preparation, the offset plates are stretched about a cylinder on an *offset* press, which works on the same principle of the old lithographic process, except that the great rotary speeds are used. Figure 194 shows an offset press.

Text Matter in processes other than letterpress printing is usually taken care of by setting type in the regular way, and photographing it to obtain a negative. It is preferable to set the type in a larger size than that wanted on the printed product, so that the detail will be sharpened when reduced in photographing. The same is true of drawings.

276. *Photo-Composing Machines*—These devices are being developed for the purpose of doing away with the pulling of proofs from type matter in reproducing type matter in offset lithography and the intaglio processes. The names of some of these machines are the Uhertype, Bagge Linophoto-type, Friedman-Bloom Photo-linotype, the Rutherford Photo-Lettering Machine, and the Orotype.

FIGURE 195—A WEBENDORFER WEB GRAVURE PRESS.

The Orotype sets lines of type and prints them on a cellophane or paper strip. The machine is operated by a keyboard, which sets type up to 14-point. Other sizes, up to 20-point, can be inserted into the machine by hand.

277. *Gravure*—This process was devised in Germany and introduced into the United States in 1912. It is an *intaglio* (in-tal′-yo) process of putting ink on paper from thousands of tiny depressions etched into the surface of a plate or cylinder. In printing, the illustrations and type matter are transferred to the paper by leaving these tiny holes, and adhering to the stock. Very fine screens make possible a multitude of tiny square dots, often numbering 160,000 to the square inch.

In *Sheet-Fed Gravure*, a copper plate is used, stretched around a cylinder; in *Rotogravure*, a copper cylinder is used.

Advantages of this process include the richness and depth of tone of illustrations, the apparent absence of any screen, the soft highlights contrasted with the deep shadows, and the ability of the process to be used on almost any type of paper stock, which is not true, generally, in the other processes of reproduction. Rich color effects are possible, and pic-

FIGURE 196—A HARRIS OFFSET PRESS.

torial sections of newspapers are printed at very high speeds, as well as catalogs and other advertising literature. Gravure, likewise, seldom needs the extra impression of black to secure the richness in colored picture shadows, as in letterpress printing.

Gravure Plates are made as follows: A negative is made of the subject to be illustrated, and a positive is produced on transparent celluloid. The positive, in which the lines are white, rather than black, is printed on a sensitized gelatin paper, called *carbon tissue*. This tissue is dampened and placed on a copper cylinder, dried, and is then ready to receive a bath of warm water, which loosens the paper backing, leaving the gelatin film on the cylinder or plate. In the shadows the film is thin, increasing as the shadows lighten.

The etching is then done in a vat of acid. The acid bites to depths depending upon the thickness of the gelatin.

Gravure Presses—Two types of gravure presses are in use: the *sheetfed* and the *rotary*. Over 10,000 impressions an hour can be turned out on the rotary press. The paper passes between a rubber impression cylinder and the plate cylinder. A *doctor*, consisting of a thin steel blade, removes the ink from the surface of the cylinder as it revolves, leaving the ink in the etched-out parts.

278. *Collotype*—This process, also known as *Photo-Gelatin*, is used for printing illustrations that appear to be an actual photographic print. It contains no screen, but otherwise appears to have the general appearance of rotogravure.

The Collotype process is especially adapted to short runs where exact photographic reproduction is wanted. The cost of the plate making is quite low, but the presswork is highly expensive, often requiring the work of three men. By a photomechanical process, a plate of glass, covered by a gelatin coating, is used directly on the press. Plates cannot be stored for future runs, as the gelatin deteriorates.

278a. *Advantages of Processes Other Than Letterpress*—In general, the processes of lithography and gravure have the following advantages over letterpress printing:

1. Greater depth of color, and faithful reproduction of illustrations.

2. Softer, more natural effect of illustrations.

3. Halftones can be reproduced on rough, mat-finished paper, eliminating the glare from stock.

4. Higher speeds in printing.

5. Press makeready not required nearly to the extent of letterpress.

6. Impressions of rules do not "show through," nor do they curl the sheet.

7. Ease of storing plates—no expensive type metal need be tied up in standing matter.

Disadvantages could be listed as:

1. The processes are not as clear nor as distinct as letterpress, especially where detail is wanted in halftones and in small sizes of type.

2. Offset plates are more easily wrecked than plates on letterpress machines.

3. More trouble is found in make-up—such as corrections after the negative has been made, as in the leading of lines, and typographical errors.

QUESTIONS FOR CLASS DISCUSSION

1. Explain briefly the process of lithography. 272.

2. Explain how offset lithography is done. 273, 274, 275.

3. In what two ways is text matter composed for offset lithography? 276.

4. What is meant by "gravure printing"? 277. What two types of this work is done? 277.

5. What is the collotype process? 278.

6. Discuss the advantages of offset printing over letterpress. 278a.

7. Discuss the disadvantages of offset printing as compared with letterpress. 278a.

BOOKS FOR FURTHER READING

CUMMINGS, "Handbook of Lithography."
GOODMAN, "Metalithography."
RHODES, "Art of Lithography."
ST. JOHN, "Rotary Web Presswork."

CHAPTER XIX

PAPER

279. Before the papermaking machine was invented in 1804 by the Fourdrinier brothers in England, all paper was made by hand. The first hand-made paper is said to have been made by the Chinese about 105 B.C. The Egyptians were making a paper of a very crude sort from the papyrus plant in 3000 B.C.

280. Most paper is made by the following process:

1. Source of raw material—Trees are cut down in the northern forests, and conveyed to the paper mill, usually by water. Paper may be made from a great many vegetable fibers, however. The last to be added to the list is corn stalks. The better grades of paper are made from linen and cotton fibers, usually obtained from the scraps of cotton mills. Spruce and hemlock are the woods best adapted to the making of paper. Southern slash pine was recently added.

2. Chipping—After the bark and knots have been removed, the log is fed against a great revolving disc upon which large sharp knives are mounted, and is cut into small chips. The chips are screened to remove all dust and to secure proper size, and stored until ready to be "digested." Figure 197.

3. Digesting—In great tile-lined digesters, the chips are cooked with calcium bisulphate and steam. This process dissolves all rosin and other binding materials, and leaves only the cellulose fibers, or "pulp." Figure 198.

4. Cleaning—All knots, pieces of bark and dirt are re-

moved by the "riffler." After being cleaned, the pulp is
bleached in chloride of lime. Figure 199.

FIGURE 197—CHIPPING LOGS IN A PAPER MILL.

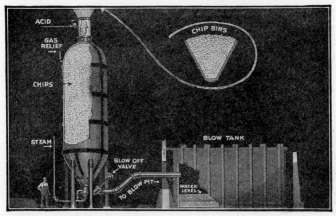

FIGURE 198—DIGESTERS IN A PAPER MILL.

5. Beating—To make the fibers of the pulp suitable for
making paper, they are beaten in water, coloring matter,

and rosin size in the "beaters." Refining engines further
treat the pulp in practically the same manner.   Figure 200

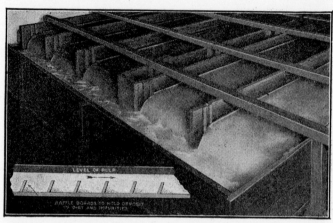

FIGURE 199—A RIFFLER.

FIGURE 200—PAPER PULP BEATERS.

6. The Papermaking Machine—On a Fourdrinier paper-
making machine, the pulp is diluted in a large quantity of

water, and is allowed to flow onto a continuous belt made of
fine wire screen. The water drains away as the screen passes

FIGURE 201—THE ROLL END OF A FOURDRINIER PAPERMAKING MACHINE.

FIGURE 202—CUTTING MACHINES IN A PAPER MILL.

through the machine. By shaking the screen, the fibers of
the pulp are laid both crosswise and lengthwise of the sheet,

which strengthens the paper. The pulp finally forms a wet sheet made up of millions of little fibers adhering tenaciously together. Heavy rollers compress the paper, and steam rollers dry it. Two "calender" rollers at the end of the machine press the paper and give it the required finish. The finished

FIGURE 203—A POWER CUTTING MACHINE.

product is wound into great rolls at the end of the machine at a speed of about five miles an hour.   Figure 201.

To make flat sheets of paper the rolls are put on large cutting machines which cut it into sheets. The paper is then inspected, and packed for shipment.   Figure 202.

281. *Watermarks*—Watermarked paper is passed under a "dandy roll" on which a design or lettering is raised in very thin wire. The wire is pressed into the pulp, making the paper thinner at that place. Watermarks may readily be seen by holding a sheet of paper to the light. Watermarking is done on writing, bond, ledger, and some antique book papers.

282. *Deckle*—A "deckle edge" is made by directing a stream of water on the edge of the pulp sheet at the mill, which leaves a feathered edge. This is also done mechanically, after the paper is made.

This edge approximates that of the natural feathered edge of hand-made paper, and is sometimes used in book printing and often on certain stationery work.

283. *Kinds of Paper*—The paper mills are attempting to classify paper in grades of 1, 2, 3, and 4 for coated stocks, and a, b, c, d, and e for uncoated stocks. This classification is for the purpose of allowing the buyer some comparison of the papers made by the various mills.

Although not a complete classification, the following will suffice for study:

1. Absorbent.   6. News.
2. Boards.   7. Printing.
3. Building.   8. Tissue.
4. Cardboards.   9. Wrapping.
5. Covers.   10. Writing.

Each paper named in the above classification is further divided into weights, sizes and finishes. The table, "Classification of Paper," in this chapter, presents the names, the special property of each kind, their uses, and usual sizes.

Because of the fact that there exists approximately 7,000 different kinds of paper stocks as well as about 3,000 minor variations, an entirely complete classification is impossible in a book of this kind.

CLASSIFICATION OF PAPER STOCK

Name	Property	Use	Sizes	
Antique book	Bulky, rough	Books, programs, advertising	25×38	28×40
			32×44	35×45
			38×50	
Blanks	Thick, smooth finish	Signs, etc.	22×28	
Blotter	Absorbent one or both sides, plate, pasted, enameled	Advertising	19×24	24×38
Bond	Rough, no glare, takes writing ink	Stationery, office forms	17×22	19×24
			22×34	
Cardboard	Heavy, durable	Cards, signs, boxes	22×28	28×44
			22½×28½	
Cellophane	Transparent	Wrappers		
Coated book	Smooth, shiny	Halftone printing	25×38	28×44
			35×45	32×44
			38×50	
Cover	Strong, easy folding	Announcements, booklets, catalogs, pamphlet covers	20×26	23×35
			22½×28½	26×40
			25×38	28×44
Eggshell book	Eggshell appearance	Books, booklets, programs, etc.	32×44	35×45
English finish	No glare, slightly roughened finish	Catalogs, booklets, magazines	25×38	28×42
			35×45	28×44
			32×44	38×50
Enameled	Shiny, smooth	Books and booklets with fine screened halftones; catalogs	25×38	35×45
			28×44	38×50
			29×52	32×44
Flats	Takes writing ink	Writing papers	17×22	17×28
			22×34	19×24
Glassine	Transparent	Wrappers, covers		
Gummed	Gummed one side	Stickers, labels	17×22	20×25
Index Bristol	Writable qualities, thick	Filing cards, records	25½×30½	

Paper	Characteristics	Uses	Flat 24×36	Rolls
India	Thin, opaque	Bibles, encyclopedias		
Kraft	Tough, thin, usually brown	Wrapping paper		
Ledgers	Take writing ink, strong	Blank books, office forms	16×21, 18×23, 21×32, 23×36, 25×38, 28×40	17×22, 19×24, 22×34, 24×38, 32×44, 38×50
Machine finish	Nonglare, smooth, book paper	Magazines, papers, advertising matter	35×45	35×45
Manifold	Thin, strong	Duplicate copies, sales books, etc.	17×22, 17×28	19×24, 28×34
Mimeograph	Roughened surface	Use in duplicating machines	17×22	17×28
Newsprint	Rough, quick drying of ink	Newspaper, handbills, posters	22×30, 22×35, 25×38, 28×42	22×32, 24×36, 26×40, 30×44, 32×44
Offset	Roughened, heavy	Advertising, books, booklets, posters	25×38, 28×42, 35×45	35×45, 32×44, 38×50
Onionskin	Thin almost to transparency	Typewritten carbon copies, wrappers	17×22, 19×24	17×26, 17×28, 28×34
Safety Paper	Designed to make forgery impossible	Checks, bonds, etc.	17×22	17×28, 19×28
Supercalendered book	Smooth	Magazines and booklets	25×38, 32×44	28×44, 35×45, 38×50
Tagboard	Tough, strong	Tags, etc.	24×36	22½×28½

(From an article by the author in *Industrial Arts and Vocational Education*)

Kinds of Printing Paper—There are many different styles and kinds of paper, so many, in fact, that it is impossible to mention all here. The most frequently used papers, however, are mentioned in the following paragraphs:

Newsprint—This is one of the cheapest grades of paper, and is made almost entirely of ground wood pulp. This "news stock" is used chiefly by newspapers, and for printing posters, circulars, and such work.

Book Paper—Several classes of book papers are used, the most frequently used being "machine finish," "supercalendered," "enameled," and "antique."

English finish book stock is usually made of sulphite soda pulp, and is the least expensive of book papers.

Supercalendered book paper has a gloss finish, and is made of practically the same materials as machine finish paper. This stock, as the first mentioned, is used chiefly for booklets, pamphlets, and similar printed matter.

Enameled paper is coated with a mixture of clay and casein glue, which gives a very high gloss to the surface of the stock. This paper is especially adapted to the printing of halftone work.

Writing papers consist of ledgers and bonds, and are made to take writing ink suitably. Writing papers are usually made from spruce and sulphite. Bonds are used for stationery, while the ledgers, being quite heavy, are used for blank book sheets.

Cardboard is made from wood and straw. Some cardboards are made to the required thickness on the machine, while others are made up of sheets of paper pasted together, the number of sheets being indicated by the thicknesses, as 2-ply, 3-ply, 10-ply, etc.

Cover papers are usually heavier, softer, and rougher

than other papers. The most used are antique, laid, ripple, plate, and wove finish. As indicated by the name, cover papers are used for covers on booklets, for menus, and such work, where stiffness, durability and beauty are required.

283a. *Grain of Paper*—The fibers which make up a sheet of machine-made paper lie to a large degree in the same general direction, due to the flowing of pulp on a traveling screen which forms the sheet. This grain must be considered in the planning of a printed job. More information will be found in paragraph 289.

Laid paper is watermarked with lines running with the grain of the sheet. Wove paper has fine lines running in both directions.

284. *Standardization of Papers*—One thousand sheets is the basis of count and weight of printing papers. The "substance weight" is the weight of 1000 sheets, and is indicated after the size of the paper listed, as 25 by 38—100; that is, 1000 sheets of this stock weigh 100 pounds. If 1000 sheets weigh 40 pounds, the paper is referred to as "substance 40"; if it weighs 16 pounds, it is "substance 16," and so on.

285. *Sizes of Paper Stock*—The standard sizes of paper stock are usually as follows: book paper, 26 by 29, 25 by 38, 32 by 44, 35 by 45 inches, and their doubles. Bonds, ledgers, and writing papers, 17 by 22, 17 by 28, 19 by 24 inches, and their doubles. (See "Classification of Paper Stock.")

286. *Cutting Paper Stock*—As paper stock is bought in large, standard sizes, it must necessarily be cut to smaller sizes needed to print the various jobs that come to hand. This cutting is done on the "paper cutter." Figure 203.

A paper cutter has a movable gauge, which may be set in inches to various measures by the small wheel near the operator's hand. The clamp which holds the paper while it is being cut is operated by a large wheel at the top of the machine. The handle that controls the blade is grasped near the upper end and moved downward, which cuts the paper. Automatic cutters are used in plants where a great amount of cutting and trimming is done. The knife blade, and often the clamp, are operated automatically by power.

Paper should be "jogged," that is, straightened, before being cut. Care must also be taken to see that the paper is placed snugly against the back gauge of the cutter. These precautions will insure the sheets being cut uniformly.

When expensive or soft paper is cut, it is necessary to place waste sheets of tag board or similar inexpensive material at the top and bottom of the pile to prevent the sheets from soiling or retaining the impression of the clamp.

287. *Figuring Paper Cutting*—In cutting paper, it is necessary to figure how many pieces of the required size can be cut from the large sheets of standard size. For instance, stock for 2000 letterheads, size $8\frac{1}{2}$ by 11 inches, is needed. The standard size is 17 by 22 inches. The number of the large sheets needed to produce 2000 letterheads is computed as follows:

$$\frac{\overset{2\times 2}{\cancel{N}\times \cancel{22}}}{\cancel{8\frac{1}{2}}\times \cancel{N}} = 4 \text{ pieces, size } 8\frac{1}{2}\times 11,$$

can be cut from one sheet 17×22 inches. Figuring the number of sheets needed:

$$2000\div 4 = 500 \text{ sheets } 17\times 22 \text{ inches}$$

are needed to make 2000 pieces $8\frac{1}{2}$ by 11 inches. Figure 204 illustrates this computation.

Another example: 1000 pieces 6×9 inches are needed. The stock size is 25×38 inches. Fractions are not considered, as they will not make a sheet that can be used:

$$\frac{\overset{4\times4}{\cancel{25\times38}}}{\cancel{6\times9}} = 16 \text{ pieces, size } 6\times9 \text{ inches,}$$

can be cut from a sheet 25×38 inches, with waste pieces

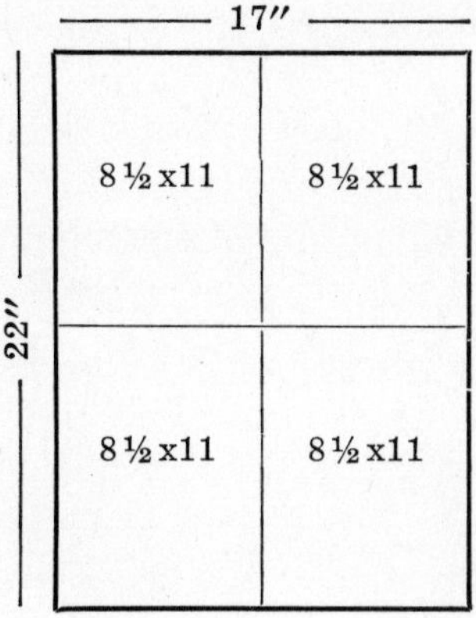

FIGURE 204—ILLUSTRATING HOW FOUR SHEETS, 8½×11 INCHES, CAN BE CUT FROM A SHEET 17×22 INCHES.

1×36 and 2×25 inches. Figuring the number of sheets needed:

1000÷16=63 sheets, 25×38 inches,

are needed to produce 1000 pieces 6×9 inches. A diagram of this computation is shown in Figure 205.

In figuring paper stock one must try the division both ways to determine which way will give the most pieces from the large sheet. An example of this type of computation follows:

Problem: How many pieces 5×9 inches can be cut from a sheet $22\frac{1}{2} \times 28\frac{1}{2}$ inches?

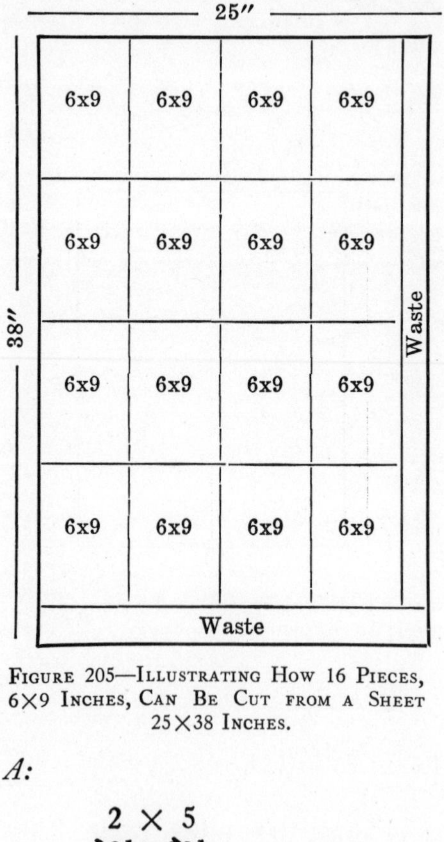

FIGURE 205—ILLUSTRATING HOW 16 PIECES, 6×9 INCHES, CAN BE CUT FROM A SHEET 25×38 INCHES.

Solution A:

$$\frac{\overset{2}{22\frac{1}{2}} \times \overset{5}{28\frac{1}{2}}}{\underset{9}{5} \times \underset{9}{9}} = 10 \text{ pieces,}$$

with waste pieces $4\frac{1}{2} \times 28\frac{1}{2}$ inches and $3\frac{1}{2} \times 18$ inches.

Solution B:

$$\frac{\overset{4}{\cancel{22\frac{1}{2}}} \times \overset{3}{\cancel{28\frac{1}{2}}}}{\cancel{5} \times \cancel{9}} = 12 \text{ pieces,}$$

with waste pieces $2\frac{1}{2} \times 28\frac{1}{2}$ inches and $1\frac{1}{2} \times 20$ inches.

Solution *B*, it is readily seen, gives two more pieces from the stock size than Solution *A*. These computations are illustrated in Figure 206.

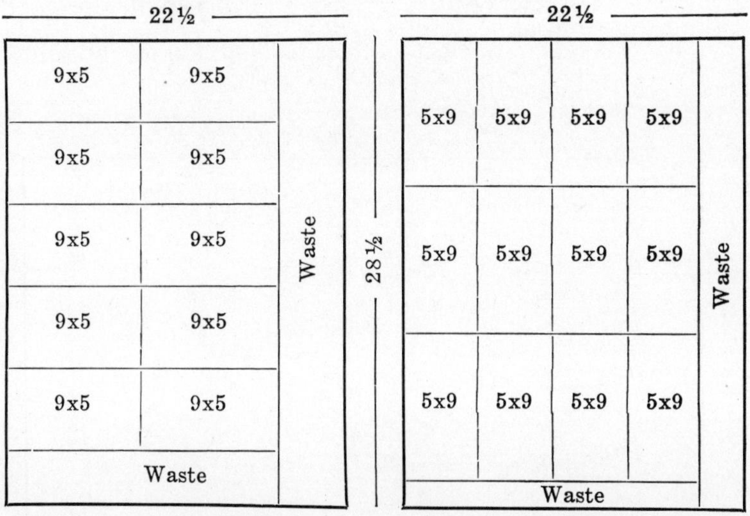

FIGURE 206—ILLUSTRATING HOW TWO MORE PIECES CAN BE CUT FROM A SHEET BY REVERSING THE DIVISION.

For the sake of economy, if waste pieces are very large, figure this spoilage to see if more pieces can be had. The following is an example of figuring the waste:

Problem: How many pieces 8×12 inches can be cut from a sheet 32×44 inches?

$$\frac{\overset{4\times3}{\cancel{32}\times\cancel{44}}}{\cancel{8}\times\cancel{12}}=12 \text{ pieces,}$$

with waste 8× 32 inches. Then figuring the waste,

$$\frac{\overset{1\times2}{\cancel{8}\times\cancel{32}}}{\cancel{8}\times\cancel{12}}=2 \text{ sheets from the waste piece}$$

Then,

$$12+2=14 \text{ pieces, size } 8\times12 \text{ inches,}$$

can be cut from one sheet 32×44 inches. Figure 207 illustrates this computation.

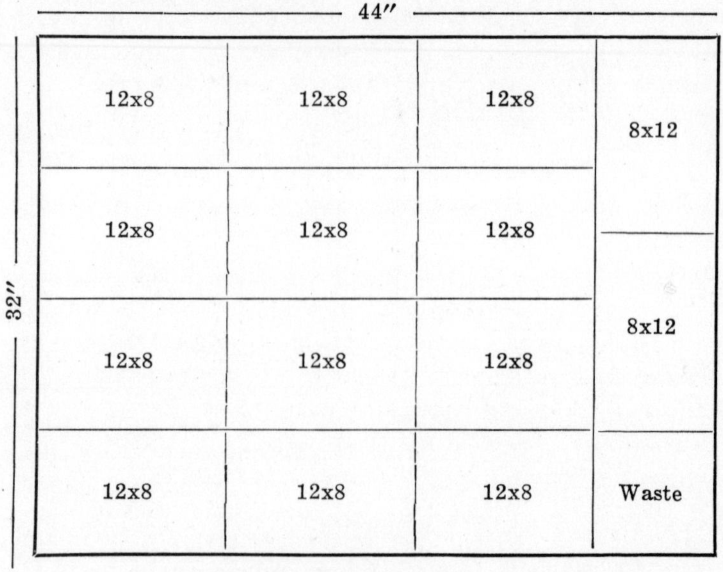

FIGURE 207—ILLUSTRATING HOW WASTE PIECES MAY BE UTILIZED IN CUTTING PAPER.

288. *Figuring for Equal Weights and Cost of Stock*—Very often a printer wants to buy a stock that is of the same basic weight as 25×38—140 (M), or a 70-pound stock, in a larger size, possibly 32×44 inch. Some paper house catalogs tabulate this weight with the size; others do not.

In calculating the ream weight of any size sheet for a given basis, as above, find the area of the two sheets in inches: 25×38 = 950 square inches; 32×44 = 1408 square inches. Now multiply the area of the ream of the unknown weight by the known ream weight: 1408×70 = 98,560. Divide this product by the area of the given weight ream: 98,560÷950 = 103.7, and for easy figuring, call this 104 pounds.

Figuring for Cost—To find the cost of a required amount of paper, multiply the number of sheets wanted by the weight of 1000 sheets; then multiply this product by the price of the stock per pound, and point off five places. For example, 850 sheets 25×38—140 (M), at $9\frac{1}{2}$ cents per pound: 850×140 = 119000×$9\frac{1}{2}$ = 1130500, and pointing off five places, this leaves $11.30 as the cost of 850 sheets, the cost price.

289. *Testing Paper*—If the run of the grain of a paper stock is not known, cut off a square piece and bend it in one hand between the fingers and thumb, both ways—the short and the long way of the large sheet. It folds easier with the grain than against the grain. There is no set rule, usually, how the grain of a stock runs, as this is dependent upon the manner in which the paper is rolled at the mill.

Another test is by tearing the sheet, which tears easily with the grain, and harder against the grain. Still another way is by wetting both sides of a piece torn from the sheet —the curl made as the paper dries will be across the grain.

In testing paper for halftone printing, look at it through a strong magnifying glass. If the fibers are compact, the paper is good for this purpose. If a grainy surface shows, it is not so good for printing halftones.

A good reflection of light from a stock does not always mean that the paper is smooth and compact. Let the light strike the paper at a 45° angle to the line of vision, and this throws into relief all of the surface irregularities.

The grain of a paper works best if it runs across the cylinder of a press. In printing index cards that are to be used in a typewriter, the grain should run along the rubber roll.

290. *Humidity*—The curling, shrinking, and stretching of paper causes trouble on printing presses. These changes in paper are due to its fibrous construction, and to the changes in the humidity of the room in which it is placed.

If the stock curls around the felt side of the paper, the humidity is high; if it curls around the wire side, the humidity is low. Paper stocks of all kinds are usually made at humidity of 50 per cent. A change from this may cause register trouble in color printing.

Paper should be seasoned for at least forty-eight hours in the pressroom where it is to be printed, so that it can become acclimated to the atmosphere of the pressroom. Many pressrooms are now air-conditioned.

QUESTIONS FOR CLASS DISCUSSION

1. From what materials is paper made?   208.
2. Explain the process of preparing the paper pulp.   280.
3. Explain the process of making pulp into sheets of paper. 280.
4. What are watermarks? How are they put into paper? 281.
5. What is meant by a "deckle edge"? How is this done? 282.
6. For what classes of work is newsprint used?   283.
7. Name four classes of book paper, and tell the use of each. 283.

8. Name two classes of writing papers, and tell the use of each. 283.

9. Explain how cardboard is made. 283.

10. What is meant by the term "substance weight"? 284.

11. Explain the standardization of papers. 284.

12. What is meant by "jogging"? 286.

13. How many pieces $5\frac{1}{2} \times 8\frac{1}{2}$ inches can be cut from a sheet 17×22 inches? 287.

14. How many pieces $8\frac{1}{2} \times 7$ inches can be cut from a sheet 17×22 inches? 287.

15. How many sheets 19×24 inches are required to make 1500 pieces 3×6 inches? 287.

16. How many sheets 25×38 inches are required to make 520 pieces 12×18 inches? 287.

17. How many pieces of cover stock 20×26 inches are needed to print 300 book covers, size 9×12 inches? 287.

18. How many pieces 10×14 inches can be cut from a sheet 25×38 inches? 287.

19. How many sheets $22\frac{1}{2} \times 28\frac{1}{2}$ inches are needed to get 1100 pieces $3\frac{1}{4} \times 6\frac{1}{2}$ inches? 287.

20. How many sheets 25×38 inches are required to make 10,000 pieces $7\frac{1}{4} \times 13$ inches?

21. What are the ten different kinds of paper stock? 283.

22. How does one figure for equal weights of various sizes of paper stock? 288.

23. In how many ways can paper be tested for grain? 289.

24. What type of paper is good for the printing of halftones? How is this paper tested? 289.

25. What effect has high humidity on paper? Low humidity? 290.

26. How is an odd number of sheets figured for the cost price? 288.

BOOKS FOR FURTHER READING

GINSBACH, "Printshop Mathematics," Manual Arts Press.
GRESS, "Handbook of Printing," Pages 131 to 136.
HACKLEMAN, "Commercial Engraving and Printing."
HAGUE, "Printshop Mathematics," Bruce Publishing Co.
MANSFIELD, "Everyday Arithmetic for Printers."
U. T. A. LIBRARY, Vols. 10 and 13.
WATT, "The Art of Papermaking."
WHEELRIGHT, "From Paper Mill to Pressroom."

Chapter XX

ACCIDENT AND HEALTH HAZARDS

291. *Printers Are Healthy*—Printers, as a group, are fairly healthy. Through surveys taken by the United States Government, it was found that "long and continuous employment in the printing trades is not incompatible with reasonably good health."

Students who decide to take up one of the printing trades, and who do much work in the school shop, should certainly be cognizant of the accident and health hazards found in the trades. For this reason, the following outline for easy study and reference has been prepared. If these hazards, their results, and each preventive is learned, these boys and girls will have a foreknowledge of what hazardous machines to watch carefully, and how to conduct themselves so that they will not fall ill.

ACCIDENT HAZARDS

Hazard	Result	Preventive
Platen presses	Crushed hands or fingers	Install proper guards; do not try to feed very small or odd-shaped sheets; do not reach for falling sheets.
Cylinder and rotary presses	Crushed or cut hands or feet	Guard all hand and foot hazards; get aid when removing and placing rollers.
Saws and saw trimmers	Mangled hands, injuries to eyes	Use guards and work holders at all times.
Composing machines	Burns, mangled hands	See that all automatic stops work correctly; do not throw pigs of metal into pot; guard molds, gears, and belts.

205

ACCIDENT HAZARDS—*Continued*

Hazard	Result	Preventive
Paper cutters	Loss of fingers or hand	Work alone when cutting paper; do not catch scrap as it comes from the knife; see that non-repeating devices work properly.
Slug cutters, mitering machines, etc.	Crushed, torn, or cut fingers or hands	Take great care on unguarded machines; use guards when provided.
Littered floors	Tripping and falling	Keep floors free from wastepaper.
Oily floors	Tripping and falling	Do not allow machines to leak oil onto floor.
Sleeves, ties, trousers, smocks	Getting caught and injured by gears, shafts, or other moving parts	Do not wear a long tie, loose, flapping sleeves or trousers, roll sleeves and trousers on inside.
Lifting forms	Rupture, strains	Get aid in lifting heavy forms.
Unguarded belts, shafts, gears	Being caught and injured	See that all belt and gear hazards are well guarded.
Staplers, stitchers, round-cornering machines	Crushed fingers or hands	Install guards where possible, take care in operating.
Oiling when machine is being operated	Hands smashed or cut	Do not wipe or oil machine while it is in operation.
Tripping and falling	Bruises, broken bones, in falling down or against machine	Keep all type cases closed, even when leaving them for a moment, especially the lower ones; roll trousers on the inside.
Folding machines	Getting caught in rollers, belts	See that machine is well guarded.
Fire	Burns	Use safety cans for benzine, gasoline and kerosene; do not keep stores of inflammable liquids in workroom; don't use celluloid eyeshade if you must smoke at work.
Handling paper	Paper cuts, rupture, strains	Take care of paper cuts to avoid infection; do not lift heavy paper loads.

ACCIDENT HAZARDS—*Continued*

HAZARD	RESULT	PREVENTIVE
Handling plates	Cuts on the hands	Take care in removing plates from patent base; treat wounds for infection.
Tools	Cuts, stab wounds, falls	Do not carry open spot-up knives in the pocket; do not leave tools on the floor.
Horseplay	Falling against other workmen who are operating machines; falling against or into machines	Refrain from wrestling or engaging in other play around machinery.
Talking with workmen operating machines	Getting out of time with machines and being injured	Do not talk to operators on machines.
Feeding of too difficult jobs on platens	Crushed hands or fingers	Run long, narrow jobs two or more up; do not reach through press to save a falling sheet.
Static electricity	Crushed hands or fingers	Do not attempt to feed electrically charged sheets by hand.
Using machines without instruction or permission	Various injuries	Keep shop discipline; put up danger signs.

HEALTH HAZARDS

HAZARD	RESULT	PREVENTIVE
Lead poisoning	Colic, constipation, paralysis, diseases of the heart, blood vessels and kidneys, insanity, death	Do not create lead dust by splashing pigs in the metal pot; keep type from mouth, avoid dry sweeping; do not eat in the workroom; wash hands before eating; clean nails often; do not smoke or chew while at work.
Improper ventilation	Fatigue, weakening of bodily resistance, poisoning from gas and fumes	Provide proper ventilation; keep pipe fumes and gases out of shop.
Carbon monoxide	Headache, dullness, lassitude, nervousness, insomnia, digestive ailments	Provide proper ventilation; keep pipe fumes and gases from gas-fired pots out of shop.

HEALTH HAZARDS—*Continued*

Hazard	Result	Preventive
Tuberculosis	Sickness, death	Do not use common drinking cup or towel; prohibit spitting on the floor; exercise in open air and in sunlight; get good ventilation while at work.
Benzine	Skin infections, faintness, dizziness, headache, vomiting	Provide proper ventilation; use gloves if susceptible; provide adequate washing facilities
Cleaning mixtures (anilin oil)	Convulsions, death	Provide proper ventilation, do not splash mixtures on hands or clothing; wear gloves.
Poor blood circulation	General ill health	Exercise in sunshine and open air after working hours.
Bad lighting	Impaired eyes	Provide proper light, correctly shaded.
Unclean wiping cloths	Skin infections	Use sterilized wiping cloths only.
Fatigue	Ill health	Proper rest.
Dust	Diseases of the respiratory system	Prohibit dry sweeping; clean plungers outside or in a box; do not blow out cases with bellows in the workroom.

QUESTIONS FOR CLASS DISCUSSION

1. What accident hazards are encountered in the composing room?

2. How would one go about to eliminate each of these hazards?

3. What accident hazards are encountered in the pressroom and bindery?

4. How would one go about to eliminate each of these hazards?

5. What health hazards are found in the pressrooms?

6. How would one go about to eliminate each of these health hazards?

7. What health hazards are found in the composing rooms?

8. How would one go about to eliminate each of these hazards?

Faces for Hand Composition

from American Type Founders

•

THE QUICK BROWN FOX JUMPS OVER
the quick brown fox jumps over   Onyx

THE QUICK BROWN FOX JUMPS   EMPIRE

The Quick Brown Fox Jumps Over The Lazy Dog The
the quick brown fox jumps over the lazy d   Park Avenue

THE QUICK BROWN FOX JUMPS OVER THE LAZY DOG THE Q
the quick brown fox jumps over the lazy dog the   Phenix

The Quick Brown Fox Jumps Over The Lazy Do
the quick brown fox jumps ove   Kaufmann Script

The Quick Brown Fox Jumps Over The La
the quick brown fox jumps   Kaufmann Bold

THE QUICK BROWN FOX JUMPS OVER
the quick brown fox jumps ov   Othello

THE QUICK BROWN FO   STYMIE MEDIUM TITLE

THE QUICK BROWN FOX JUMPS OVER T
the quick brown fox jump   Stymie Medium

THE QUICK BROWN FOX JUMPS OV
the quick brown fox ju   Stymie Black

THE QUICK BROWN FOX JUMPS OVE
the quick bro   Century Schoolbook Bold

THE QUICK BROWN FOX JUMPS OVER
the quick brown fox j   Schoolbook Oldstyle

THE QUICK BROWN FOX JUMPS OVER T
the quick brown fox jumps ov   Goudy Oldstyle

THE QUICK BROWN FOX JUMPS OVE
the quick brown fox ju   Goudy Handtooled

THE QUICK BROWN FOX JUMPS OVE
the quick brown fox jumps ove   Goudy Bold

THE QUICK BROWN FOX JUMPS OV
the quick brown fox ju   Goudy Extrabold

THE QUICK BROWN FOX JUMPS OVER THE LAZ
the quick brown fox jumps over the lazy do   Garamond

THE QUICK BROWN FOX JUMPS OVER THE L
the quick brown fox jumps over t   Garamond Bold

HUXLEY VERTICAL

THE QUICK BROWN SHADOW

THE QUICK BROWN FOX JUMPS OVER THE L
the quick brown fox jumps o   Bernhard Gothic Light

THE Q · BERNHARD GOTHIC MEDIUM TITLE

THE QUICK BROWN FOX JUMPS OVER TH
the quick brown fox ju   Bernhard Gothic Heavy

THE QUICK BROWN FOX JUMPS OVER T
the quick bro   Bernhard Gothic Extra Heavy

THE QUICK BROWN FOX JUMPS O
the quick brown fox jumps over the la   Bernhard Fashion

THE QUICK BROWN FOX JUMPS OVER THE LAZY DOG THE QU
the quick brown fox jumps over the lazy dog the quick   Tower

THE QUICK BROWN FOX JUMP
the   Bulletin Typewriter

THE QUICK BROWN FOX JUMPS OVER THE
the quick brown fox jumps ove   Stymie Light

THE QUICK BROWN FOX JUMPS OVER TH
the quick brown fox jumps   Caslon Oldstyle No. 471

THE QUICK BROWN FOX JUMPS OV
the quick brown fox jumps ov   Caslon Openface

THE QUICK BROWN FOX JUMPS OV
the quick brown fox jumps   Caslon Bold

THE QUICK BROWN FOX JUMPS OVER
the quick brown fox jumps over the lazy   Nicolas Cochin

The Quick Brown Fox Jumps Over The Lazy Dog The Q
the quick brown fox jumps over the lazy dog   Wedding Text

The Quick Brown Fox Jumps Over The Lazy Dog The Quick Brow
the quick brown fox jumps over the lazy dog   Typo Script Extended

THE QUICK BROWN FOX JUMPS O
the quick brown fox jumps over   Bernhard Tango

THE QUICK BROWN FOX JUMPS OVER THE LA
the quick brown fox jumps over the lazy do   Bodoni

THE QUICK BROWN FOX JUMPS OVER THE LA
the quick brown fox jumps over the laz   Bodoni Italic

THE QUICK BROWN FOX JUMPS OVER THE L
the quick brown fox jumps over the   Bodoni Bold

THE QUICK BROWN FOX JUMPS O
the quick brown   Ultra Bodoni Italic

Faces for Machine or Hand Composition

From Lanston Monotype Machine Company

THE QUICK BROWN FOX JUMPS OVER THE L
the quick brown fox jumps over the lazy   Deepdene 315

THE QUICK BROWN FOX JUMPS OVER THE LAZY
the quick brown fox jumps over the lazy   *Deepdene Italic 3151*

THE QUICK BROWN FOX JUMPS OVER THE LAZY D
the quick brown fox jumps over the   Stymie Light 190

THE QUICK BROWN FOX JUMPS OVER TH
the quick brown fox   Stymie Light Italic 1901

THE QUICK BROWN FOX JUMPS OVER THE
the quick brown fox jumps over Stymie Bold 189

THE QUICK BROWN FOX JUMPS OVER
the quick brown   Stymie Bold Italic 1891

THE QUICK BROWN FOX JUMPS OVER THE L
the quick brown fox jum   Stymie Extrabold 390

THE QUICK BROWN FOX JUMPS OVE
the quic Stymie Extrabold Italic 3901

THE QUICK BROWN FOX JUMPS OVER THE LAZY DOG THE
the quick brown fox jumps over 20th Century Medium 605

THE QUICK BROWN FOX JUMPS OVER THE LAZY
the quick brown fox jumps over the lazy   Baskerville Italic 3531

THE QUICK BROWN FOX JUMPS OVER THE LAZ
the quick brown fox jumps over the   Binny Oldstyle 21

THE QUICK BROWN FOX JUMPS OVER THE LAZ
the quick brown fox jumps ove   Binny Oldstyle Italic 2111

THE QUICK BROWN FOX JUMPS OVER THE LAZY
the quick brown fox jumps over the lazy dog   Bodoni 375

THE QUICK BROWN FOX JUMPS OVER THE LAZY
the quick brown fox jumps over the lazy   Bodoni Italic 3751

THE QUICK BROWN FOX JUMPS OVER THE LA
the quick brown fox jumps over   Bodoni Bold 275

THE QUICK BROWN FOX JUMPS OVER THE LA
the quick brown fox jum   Bodoni Bold Italic 2751

THE QUICK BROWN FOX JUMPS OVER
the quick brown fox   Ultra Bodoni 675

THE QUICK BROWN FOX JUMPS OVE
the quick brow   Ultra Bodoni Italic 6751

THE QUICK BROWN FOX JUMPS OVER THE LA
the quick brown fox jumps over t   Caslon Bold 79

THE QUICK BROWN FOX JUMPS OVER THE LAZ
the quick brown fox jumps   Caslon Bold Italic 791

Intertype Faces

INTERTYPE FACES ARE MADE ON MODERN WIDE TOOTH MATRIC
Intertype faces are made on modern wide tooth matrices. These Vogue

INTERTYPE FACES ARE MADE ON MODERN WIDE TOOTH MAT
Intertype faces are made on modern wide tooth matrices.   Cairo

INTERTYPE FACES ARE MADE ON MODERN WIDE TOOTH MA
Intertype faces are made on modern wide tooth matrices. These Garamond

INTERTYPE FACES ARE MADE ON MODERN WIDE TOOTH
Intertype faces are made on modern wide tooth matrices.   Baskerville

INTERTYPE FACES ARE MADE ON MODERN WIDE TOOTH MAT
Intertype faces are made on modern wide tooth matrices.   Bodoni Book

INTERTYPE FACES ARE MADE ON MODERN WIDE TOOTH MATRIC
Intertype faces are made on modern wide tooth matrice Beton Medium

INTERTYPE FACES ARE MADE ON MODERN WIDE TOO
Intertype faces are made on modern wide tooth matrices. Ideal

INTERTYPE FACES ARE MADE ON MODERN WIDE TOO
Intertype faces are made on modern wide tooth matrices. Regal

INTERTYPE FACES ARE MADE ON MODERN WIDE TOO
Intertype faces are made on modern wide tooth matrices. Bookface

INTERTYPE FACES ARE MADE ON MODERN WIDE TOOTH M
Intertype faces are made on modern wid Vogue Bold Cond.

INTERTYPE FACES ARE MADE ON MO
Intertype faces are made on Vogue Bold

INTERTYPE FACES ARE MADE ON MODERN WI
Intertype faces are made on mo Bodoni Bold Cond.

INTERTYPE FACES ARE MADE ON M
Intertype faces are made on Beton Bold

INTERTYPE FACES ARE MADE ON
Intertype faces are made o Goudy Bold

INTERTYPE FACES ARE MADE ON
Intertype faces are made Medieval Bold

INTERTYPE FACES ARE MADE ON MOD
Intertype faces are made on mode Vogue

INTERTYPE FACES ARE MADE ON M
Intertype faces are made on mo Cairo

INTERTYPE FACES ARE MADE ON M
Intertype faces are made on moder Bodoni

INTERTYPE FACES ARE MADE ON M
Intertype faces are made Garamond Bold

INTERTYPE FACES ARE MADE ON M
Intertype faces are made o Bodoni Bold

INTERTYPE FACES ARE MADE ON
Intertype faces are made o Cairo Bold

INTERTYPE FACES ARE MADE ON MODERN W
Intertype faces are made on Vogue Extra Bold

INTERTYPE FACES ARE MADE ON
Intertype faces are n Bodoni Modern

INTERTYPE FACES ARE MADE ON MOD
Intertype faces are ma Beton Extra Bold

Specimens of Linotype Faces

THE QUICK BROWN FOX JUMPS OVER THE LAZY DOG THE Q
the quick brown fox jumps over the lazy dog   **Excelsior Bold—8**

THE QUICK BROWN FOX JUMPS OVER THE LAZY DOG THE Q
the quick brown fox jumps over the lazy dog the   Excelsior—8

THE QUICK BROWN FOX JUMPS OVER THE LAZY DOG THE Q
the quick brown fox jumps over the lazy dog the   Ideal—8

THE OUICK BROWN FOX JUMPS OVER THE LAZY DOG THE Q
the quick brown fox jumps over the lazy dog the   *Ideal Italic—R*

THE QUICK BROWN FOX JUMPS OVER THE LAZY DOG THE Q
the quick brown fox jumps over the lazy dog the   **Ideal Bold—8**

THE QUICK BROWN FOX JUMPS OVER THE LAZY
the quick brown fox jumps over the lazy   Garamond—12

THE QUICK BROWN FOX JUMPS OVER THE LAZY
the quick brown fox jumps over the   *Garamond Italic—12*

THE QUICK BROWN FOX JUMPS OVER THE LAZY DO
the quick brown fox jumps over the   Scotch Roman—11

THE QUICK BROWN FOX JUMPS OVER THE LAZY DO
the quick brown fox jumps over the   *Scotch Italic—11*

THE QUICK BROWN FOX JUMPS OVER
the quick brown fox jumps over   Century—14

THE QUICK BROWN FOX JUMPS OVER
the quick brown fox   **Cheltenham Bold—14**

THE QUICK BROWN FOX JUMPS OVER THE LA
the quick brown fox jumps over Metromedium—14

THE QUICK BROWN FOX JUMPS OVER THE LA
the quick brown fox jumps over   Metrothin—14

THE QUICK BROWN FOX JUMPS OVER THE LAZY DOG
the quick brown fox jumps Erbar Light Condensed–18

THE QUICK BROWN FOX JUMPS OVER THE LAZY DOG
the quick brown fox jumps Erbar Bold Condensed–18

THE QUICK BROWN FOX JU
the quic Metromedium Italic 24

THE QUICK BROWN FOX JU
the quick bro Metromedium 24

THE QUICK BROWN FOX JUMPS
the Century Bold Condensed--30

Specimens of Ludlow Typefaces

Tempo Light

Printers Endorse the Ludlow

Karnak Light

Organize a Printers Guild

Karnak Intermediate

Newspaper Display Head

Karnak Medium

Exhibit of Fine Printing to be held in the Library

Karnak Obelisk

Sale of Fine Irish Linens

Karnak Black

A Powerful Italic Type

Karnak Black Italic

Great Demand for Modern Designs

Karnak Black Condensed

A Typeface Designed for Display

Tempo Light Italic

Costs are cut by Installing a Ludlow

Tempo Medium

Students Learn the Ludlow System

Tempo Medium Italic

Interesting Types on Display

Tempo Bold

A New Edition is Entirely Set by Hand

Tempo Bold Condensed

Ideal for Newspaper Heads

Tempo Heavy

New Type for Display Work

Tempo Heavy Italic

Modern Printers Use Ludlow System

Eden Light

Advertisers Use this New Design

Eden Bold

The Ludlow System of Composition

Mayfair Cursive

Reduce Costs with the Ludlow

Eusebius Open

Sluglines Reduce the Make-up Time

Eusebius Light

Ludlow Full-Kerning Unbreakable Italic

Eusebius Light Italic

Art Club Elects Four New Officers

Eusebius Bold

EXERCISES AND PROBLEMS

No. 1—Setting Letters p and q

Specifications:

1. Set a stick to 13 ems.
2. Set a lead between each line.
3. Use a 3-em space between letters, and justify.
4. If the case does not have sufficient letters for a full line, quad out.

References: 40, 41, 44, 47, 49.

Copy:

p p p p p p p p p p p p p p p p p p p p p p
q q q q q q q q q q q q q q q q q q q q q q
p p p p p p p p p p p p p p p p p p p p p

No. 2—Setting Letters O, 0 and o

Specifications:

1. Set a stick to 12 ems.
2. Set a lead between each line.
3. Use a 4-em space between letters, and justify.
4. If the case does not contain sufficient letters for a full line, quad out.

References: 40, 41, 44, 47, 49.

Copy:

O O O O O O O O O O O O O O O O O
0 0 0 0 0 0 0 0 0 0 0 0 0 0 0 0 0 0 0 0
o o o o o o o o o o o o o o o o o o o o o o

No. 3—Setting Letters n and u

Specifications:

1. Set a stick to 11 ems.
2. Set a lead between each line.
3. Use a 5-em space between letters, and justify.
4. If the case does not contain sufficient letters for a full line, quad out.

References: 40, 41, 44, 47, 49.

Copy:

```
n n n n n n n n n n n n n n n n n n n
u u u u u u u u u u u u u u u u u u u
n n n n n n n n n n n n n n n n n n n
u u u u u u u u u u u u u u u u u u u
```

No. 4—Setting Letters b and d

Specifications:

1. Set a stick to 14 ems.
2. Set a lead between each line.
3. Use an en quad between each letter, and justify.
4. If the case does not contain sufficient letters for a full line, quad out.

References: 40, 41, 44, 47, 49.

Copy:

```
b b b b b b b b b b b b b b b b b b
d d d d d d d d d d d d d d d d d d
b b b b b b b b b b b b b b b b b b
d d d d d d d d d d d d d d d d d d
```

No. 5—Setting Letters l, I and 1

Specifications:

1. Set a stick to 15 ems.
2. Set a lead between each line.
3. Use an em quad between letters, and justify.
4. If the case does not contain sufficient letters for a full line, quad out.

References: 40, 41, 44, 47, 49.

Copy:

```
l l l l l l l l l l l l l l
I I I I I I I I I I I I I I
1 1 1 1 1 1 1 1 1 1 1 1 1 1
```

No. 6—Setting Figures 6 and 9

Specifications: 40, 41, 44, 47, 49.

1. Set a stick to 16 ems.
2. Set a lead between each line.
3. Use a 2-em quad between letters, and justify.

References: 40, 41, 44, 47, 49.

Copy:

6 6 6 6 6 6 · 6 6 6
9 9 9 9 9 9 9 9 9

No. 7—Setting Figures 2 and 5

Specifications:

1. Set a stick to 17 ems.
2. Set a lead between each line.
3. Use a 3-em quad between letters.

References: 40, 41, 44, 47, 49.

Copy:

2   2   2   2   2   2   2
5   5   5   5   5   5   5

No. 8—Setting a Sentence

Specifications:

1. Set a stick to 22 ems.
2. Use a 6-point slug between lines.
3. Start with 3-em spaces between *words*, and justify.   No space is set between letters.

References, in addition to those preceding: 42, 66 to 78.

Copy:

The quick brown fox jumps over the lazy dog.

The quick brown fox jumps over the lazy dog.

No. 9—Centering a Line

Specifications:

1. Set a stick to 19 ems.
2. Use a slug between each line.
3. Center *your* name and address in the manner shown in the copy.

Reference: 50.

Copy:

Your Name

Your Street Address

Your City

No. 10—Setting Points

Specifications:
1. Set your stick to 15 ems.
2. Set the type leaded (i.e., put a lead between each line).

References: 51, 54.

Copy:

> Do your work—not just your work and no
> more, but a little more the lavishing's sake;
> that little more which is worth all the rest.

No. 11—Setting Quotation

Specifications:
1. Set a stick to 16 ems.
2. Lead each line.

References: 52, 54.

Copy:

> "Every school boy and girl who has arrived at
> the age of reflection ought to know something
> about the history of the Art of Printing."—
> Horace Mann.

No. 12—Setting Caps

Specifications:
1. Set 24 ems wide, in caps, double leaded.

References: 53, 54.

Copy:

BOOK LOVE IS YOUR PASS TO THE GREATEST, THE PUR-
EST AND THE MOST PERFECT PLEASURE THAT GOD HAS
PREPARED FOR HIS CREATURES. IT LASTS WHEN ALL
OTHER PLEASURES FADE. IT WILL MAKE YOUR HOURS
PLEASANT TO YOU AS LONG AS YOU LIVE.

No. 13—Setting a Hanging Indention

Specifications:

1. Set 13 ems wide, leaded, in the hanging indention style.

Reference: 55.

Copy.

WANTED—Combination linotype operator and ad. compositor for country
weekly. Apply by letter to Box 15.

No. 14—Setting a Half-Diamond Indention

Specifications:

1. Set 24 ems wide, leaded, in half-diamond indention style.

Reference: 56

Copy:

Printing is a good business. It is clean, honorable, respectable. It is cele-
brated as a trainer of men for higher stations in life. It has many
inspiring traditions and legends. It combines the need
for knowledge of everything under the sun.

No. 15—Setting a Diagonal Indention

Specifications:

1. Set 23 ems wide, leaded, in diagonal indention style.

Reference: 57.

Copy:

The printer is brought into contact with all vocations and pro-
fessions. No vocation or profession can exist without the printing press. From text books to novels, none can evade it.

No. 16—Setting a Squared Indention

Specifications:

1. Set 24 ems wide, leaded, in square indention style, setting 5 ems of space on each side of each line.

Reference: 58.

Copy:

> To achieve success a man must attend strictly to business and keep a little in advance of the times. The man who reaches the top is not content with doing just what is required of himself—he does more!

No. 17—Setting Poetry Indention

Specifications:

1. Set 15 ems wide, leaded, indenting properly.

Reference: 59.

Copy:

> "I am not poor, but I am proud
> Of one inalienable right,
> Above the envy of the crowd,
> Thought's holy light."

No. 18—Setting Leaders

Specifications:

1. Set 16 ems wide, leaded.

Reference: 61.

Copy:

TYPE HEIGHTS

America	.918
France	.928
England	.917
Bulgaria	.928

No. 19—Multiple Justification

Specifications:

Set 15 ems wide, leaded.

References: 61, 62.

Copy:

	Games	Won	Lost
McKinley............	10	5	5
Roosevelt............	12	8	4
Harding.............	15	6	9
Lincoln.............	11	5	6

No. 20—Setting Roman Numerals

Specifications:

1. Set 14 ems wide, leaded.

Reference: 63.

Copy:

    I   Parts of a Type
    II   Kinds of Type Faces
    III The Point System
    IV   The Layout of a Type Case
    V   Learning the Case

No. 21—Setting Ditto Marks

Specifications:

1. Set 18 ems wide, leaded, using ditto marks.

References: 61, 64.

Copy:

A page containing 1000 ems pica is equal to a page containing:

10 point............................	1,190 ems
9 "	1,778 "
8 "	2,250 "
7 "	2,939 "
6 "	4,000 "

No. 22—Setting Initial Letters

Specifications:

1. Set 14 ems wide, solid, using a three-line initial, as in copy.

Reference: 65.

Copy:

> SUCCESS lies, not in achieving what you
> aim at, but in aiming at what you
> ought to achieve, and pressing forward,
> sure of achievement here, or if not here,
> in the hereafter.

No. 23—MAKING UP A 6-POINT BORDER

Specifications:

1. Make up a 6-point border from foundry material, size 16 by 21 ems.

References: 82, 87.

No. 24—MAKING UP A 12-POINT BORDER

Specifications:

1. Make up a 12-point border from foundry material, size 17 by 22 ems.

References: 82, 87.

No. 25—LINING TYPE WITH RULE

Specifications:

1. Set 20 ems wide, line brass rule harmoniously with the type as in the copy.
2. Set two slugs between each line.

Reference: 88.

Copy:

Name_____

Street Address_____

City_____

State_____

No. 26—MAKING A LAYOUT

Specifications:

1. Make a layout for the following copy, using Figure 71 as a model.

References: 90, 91, 92, 94, 109.

Copy: Mortgages, Safely Bearing Eight Per cent. We Have Loaned Millions without Loss. Smith & Harding, 140 Market Street.

No. 27—LAYING OUT AND SETTING AN ENVELOPE CORNER CARD
Specifications:
1. Make out a layout for an Executive Size envelope.
2. After receiving an OK, compose.

References: 109, 115, 117.

Copy: Johnson & Wolfe, Florists, Fifth at Washington, Toledo, Ohio.

No. 28—LAYING OUT AND SETTING A LETTERHEAD
Specifications.
1. Make out a layout for an Executive Size letterhead.
2. After receiving an OK, compose.

References: 109, 118, 119, 120.

Copy: Randolph W. Clayton, Attorney at Law, 701 State Bank Building, Cincinnati, Ohio.

No. 29—LAYING OUT AND SETTING A PERSONAL LETTERHEAD
Specifications:
1. Make a layout for a personal letterhead for yourself.
2. After receiving an OK, compose.

References: 109, 121.

Copy: To be made up by student.

No. 30—LAYING OUT AND SETTING A BUSINESS CARD
Specifications:
1. Make a layout for a No. 12 business card.
2. After receiving an OK, compose.

References: 109, 124, 125, 126.

Copy: The Paris Importing Co., Wholesale Millinery, 17 Rue de la Paix, Paris, 34 Broadway, New York.

No. 31—LAYING OUT AND SETTING A BILLHEAD
Specifications:
1. Make a layout for an $8\frac{1}{2} \times 4\frac{2}{3}$-inch billhead.
2. After receiving an OK, compose.
3. Set rules as shown in Figure 83.

References: 109, 129, 131.

Copy: The Belleville Hardware Co., Farming Implements, Main Street at Oak, Belleville, Indiana. Account of . . . ., Date . . . .

No. 32—Laying Out and Setting a Tag
Specifications:
1. Make a layout for a No. 5 tag.
2. After receiving an OK, compose.

References: 109, 137, 138, 139.

Copy: To . . . . (set three lines) The Johnston-Brewsters Co., Wholesale Grocers, 712 South Fourth St., Cleveland, Ohio.

No. 33—Laying Out and Setting a Package Label
Specifications:
1. Make a layout for a package label.
2. After receiving an OK, compose.
3. Set three rule lines for writing in address.

References: 109, 140, 141, 142.

Copy: J. S. Smith, Ltd., Iron Castings, Montreal, Canada.

No. 34—Laying Out and Setting a Ticket
Specifications:
1. Make a layout for a ticket.
2. After receiving an OK, compose.

References: 109, 132, 133, 134, 135.

Copy: "Mr. Bradley's Error," Presented by the Dramatic Club of West High School, West Auditorium, Thursday Evening at 8 o'Clock, April 6. Students 50 cents, Adults $1.00.

No. 35—Laying Out and Setting a Menu
Specifications:
1. Lay out a menu, submit, and compose.

References: 109, 143, 144, 145, 146.

Copy: Annual Banquet, Hi-Y Club, Franklin High School, April 16, 1932. Menu, Olives, Radishes, Celery, Turtle Soup, Bread Sticks, Fillet of Beef, Mashed Potatoes, Green Peas, Chicken Croquettes with Cream Sauce, Frozen Pudding, Assorted Cakes, Crackers.

No. 36—Laying Out and Setting a Program

Specifications:

1. Lay out a one-sheet program, submit, and compose.

References: 109, 147, 148, 149, 151.

Copy: "Toreadors," Presented by Harding Junior High School, Wednesday Evening, May 23, Wells Auditorium. The Cast: Señor Dictorio, Robert Smith; Toreador, Charles Bowen; Juan, William Messerly; Pablo, Ralph Stevens; Benito, Dorothy James; Maria, Gertrude Westlake; Dolores, Mary Meyers; Juanita, Helen Zimmerman. Act 1—Scene in Dictorio's garden. Act 2—Same as Act 1.

No. 37—Laying Out and Setting a Handbill

Specifications:

1. Lay out a 6×9-inch handbill, submit, and compose.

References: 109, 152, 153, 154.

Copy: Baseball, South High School versus West High School, Harding Stadium, Friday Afternoon, May 22, at 3:30. The Last Game of the Season.

No. 38—Laying Out and Setting a Wedding Announcement

Specifications:

1. Lay out a wedding announcement, submit, and compose.

References: 109, 156, 158, 159.

Copy: Mr. and Mrs. Edward White invite you to attend the marriage of their daughter, Eleanor, to Mr. Gordon W. Sprague, on Wednesday, the ninth of June, one thousand nine hundred and thirty-two, at the hour of ten. St. Francis Church, Cincinnati, Ohio.

No. 39—Laying Out and Setting a Greeting Card

Specifications:

1. Lay out a Christmas greeting card, submit, and compose.

References: 109, 160, 161.

Copy: To be made up by student.

No. 40—Laying Out and Setting a Window Card
Specifications:

1. Lay out a window card, submit, and compose.

References: 109, 164, 165.

Copy: Art Exhibit, Central High School, Syracuse, New York. January 11 to 18, from 8 A.M. to 3:30 P.M. The Public Is Invited.

No. 41—Laying Out and Setting a One-Column Advertisement
Specifications:

1. Lay out a one-column advertisement, 13-em column, submit, and compose with border.

References: 109, 166, 168, 169.

Copy: Kibling Hats, the Headgear of a Gentleman, Shown by Barnes, Inc., Sixth and Main.

No. 42—Laying Out and Setting a Two-Column Advertisement
Specifications:

1. Lay out a two-column advertisement, 12-em column, submit, and compose with border.

References: 109, 166, 167, 168, 169.

Copy: Now Is the Time to Lay in Your Coal. Pocahontas Coal Is Sold by the Black Diamond Coal Company, 1900 Front Street. Telephone ADams 4325.

No. 43—Laying Out and Setting a Book Plate

Specifications: Lay out a book plate for yourself, submit, and compose.

References: 109, 172, 173, 174.

Copy: To be made up by student.

No. 44—Laying Out and Setting Rule Forms
Specifications:

1. Lay out a rule form, 6×4 inches, submit, and compose.

References: 109, 176, 178.

Copy:

CLASS SCHEDULE

Period	Monday	Tuesday	Wednesday	Thursday	Friday
1					
2					
3					
4					
5					
6					

PROJECTS

Introduction—When student proficiency has reached a point where it is possible for them to work in most of the simple trade skills independently, the writer suggests that each works on a trial project, such as is listed in this section. Later, as the proficiency of the pupils increases, projects of their own should be incorporated.

Rating Blank—The instructor may himself, or through class discussion, rate the finished projects. A rating blank like the one below is suggested for this use.

RATING BLANK

1. Composition (kind and size of type selected and the layout) . . ____%
2. Art (color of ink, balance and harmony) . . . . ____%
3. Presswork (inking, makeready, feeding) . . . . ____%

Average . . . . ____%

How to Use This Section—In Project No. 1, note the figures after each problem to be solved, or operation to be performed. These figures refer to the particular section of the text that treats with this information. By following this outline or analysis, the pupil should safely and independently proceed with his project. Later, in projects of his own choice, he can make his own analysis sheet, using the ones following as models, and the index of the text as a guide.

THE NAME CARD

I. Layout

    1. Preparing the copy. 125.

    2. Sizes of cards. Fig. 79.

    3. Design. 126.

    4. Optical center and balance. 99, 100.

    5. Fitting the job in type. 110, Figs. 70, 80, 81.

    6. Making the layout. 106, 107, 108, 126.

        a. Display. 89, 90, 91, 92, 94.

        b. Harmony. 95, 96, 97, 98.

        c. Appropriateness. 104.

        d. Choosing the correct type face. 105.

        e. The layout procedure. 109.

II. Operations

    1. Composition

        a. Setting the stick. 40.

        b. Centering a line. 50.

        c. Justifying a line of type. 41.

        d. Removing the type from the stick. 66, Fig. 32.

        e. Tying up the type form. 67, Figs. 33, 34.

    2. Pulling a proof. 68.

    3. Locking up. 206.

    4. Inking the press. 221.

    5. Makeready. 222.

        a. Putting on a new tympan sheet. 222.

        b. Adjusting the impression. 222.

        c. Setting the guides. 223.

    6. Feeding the press. 228.

    7. Washing the press. 229.

    8. Cleaning the type form.

    9. Distributing the type. 77, 78, 79, 80.

III. Related Information
    1. Methods of manufacturing name cards
        a. Letterpress
        b. Copperplate engraving, the processes involved and comparison with other methods. 266, 267, 268.
        c. Thermography, the processes involved and the comparison with other methods. 269.
        d. Lithography, the process and comparison with other methods. 273.
    2. Paper stock. 124, 283.

IV. Judging the Job

QUESTIONS FOR CLASS DISCUSSION

1. What copy does the social card usually contain? The business card? 125.

2. What size of card is appropriate for a gentleman? A young lady? Fig. 79.

3. Where should the main display line of the card be placed? 126.

4. By what three methods are cards manufactured? Which is the most expensive? The least expensive? 266, 268, 269, 273.

5. What weight of cardboard stock is appropriate for cards? 124.

PROJECT NUMBER TWO

THE LETTERHEAD

I. Layout
    1. Preparing the copy. 120.
    2. Sizes of letterheads. 118, 121.
    3. Design. 119.
    4. Fitting the job in type. 110, Fig. 70.
    5. Making the layout. 106, 107, 108, 126.
        a. Display. 89, 90, 91, 92, 94.

b. Harmony. 95, 96, 97, 98.

c. Appropriateness. 104.

d. Choosing the correct type face. **105.**

e. The layout procedure. 109.

II. Operations

  1. Composition

      a. Setting the stick. 40.

      b. Centering a line. 50.

      c. Justifying a line of type. 41.

      d. Removing the type from the stick. 66, Fig. **32.**

      e. Tying up the type form. 67, Figs. 33, 34.

  2. Pulling a proof. 68.

  3. Locking up. 206.

  4. Inking the press. 221.

  5. Bindery.

      a. Watermarks. 281.

      b. Writing and bond papers. 283.

      c. Sizes of bond papers. 286.

      d. Figuring the stock. 285, 287.

      e. Cutting the stock. 286.

  6. Makeready. 222.

      a. Putting on a new tympan sheet. **222.**

      b. Adjusting the impression. 222.

      c. Setting the guides. 223.

  7. Feeding the press. 228.

  8. Washing the press. 229.

  9. Cleaning the type form.

 10. Distributing the type. 77, 78, 79, 80.

III. Related Information

  1. Methods of manufacturing letterheads.

      a. Letterpress.

      b. Copperplate engraving. 266, 267, 268.

      c. Thermography. 269.

      d. Lithography. 273.

IV. Judging the Job

QUESTIONS FOR CLASS DISCUSSION

1. What copy does the social letterhead usually contain? The business letterhead? 120.

2. Name one good size for business letterheads. Name one good size for social correspondence. 118, 121.

3. What size of type would be appropriate for a business letterhead? A social letterhead? 122.

4. What kind of type would be appropriate for a hardware store letterhead? A china shop letterhead? 104, 105.

5. By what methods other than letterpress are letterheads made?

PROJECT NUMBER THREE

THE ENVELOPE CORNER CARD

I. Layout
1. Preparing the copy. 114.
2. Sizes of envelopes. 115, Fig. 75.
3. Design. 117.
4. Fitting the job in type. 110, Fig. 70.
5. Making the layout. 106, 107, 108, 126.
    a. Display. 89, 90, 91, 92, 94.
    b. Harmony. 95, 96, 97, 98.
    c. Appropriateness. 104.
    d. Choosing the correct type face. 105.
    e. The layout procedure. 109.

II. Operations
1. Composition
    a. Setting the stick. 40.
    b. Centering a line. 50.
    c. Justifying a line of type. 41.
    d. Removing the type from the stick, 66, Fig. 32.
    e. Tying up the type form. 67, Figs. 33, 34.

2. Pulling a proof. 68.
3. Locking up. 206.
4. Inking the press. 221.
5. Makeready. 222.
    a. Putting on a new tympan sheet. 222.
    b. Adjusting the impression. 222.
    c. Setting the guides. 223.
6. Feeding the press. 228.
7. Washing the press. 229.
8. Cleaning the type form.
9. Distributing the type. 78, 79, 80.

III. Related Information

IV. Judging the Job

QUESTIONS FOR CLASS DISCUSSION

1. What is the primary purpose of the envelope corner card? 114.

2. What are the two most popular sizes of envelopes used for business purposes? 115.

3. What size envelope do business men prefer? 115.

4. What size letterhead goes with the $6\frac{3}{4}$ size of envelope? What size envelope should be used with the $7\frac{1}{4} \times 10\frac{1}{2}$ letterhead?

5. How large is the main display line of an envelope corner card set? 117.

6. How are very large orders of envelope corner cards often printed? 116.

Project Number Four

THE INVITATION AND ANNOUNCEMENT

I. Layout
    1. Preparing the copy. 155, 156.
    2. Sizes of announcements. 157.
    3. Designs. 159.

4. Fitting the job in type. 110, Fig. 70.
5. Making the layout. 106, 107, 108, 126.
    a. Display. 89, 90, 91, 92, 94.
    b. Harmony. 95, 96, 97, 98.
    c. Appropriateness. 104.
    d. Choosing the correct type face. 105.
    e. The layout procedure. 109.

II. Operations
  1. Composition
    a. Setting the stick. 40.
    b. Centering a line. 50.
    c. Justifying a line of type. 41.
    d. Removing the type from the stick. 66, Fig. 32.
    e. Tying up the type form. 67, Figs. 33, 34.
  2. Pulling a proof. 68.
  3. Locking up. 206.
  4. Inking the press. 221.
  5. Bindery
    a. Figuring the stock. 285, 287.
    b. Cutting the stock. 286.
  6. Makeready. 222.
    a. Putting on a new tympan sheet. 222.
    b. Adjusting the impression. 222.
    c. Setting the guides. 223.
  7. Feeding the press. 228.
  8. Washing the press. 229.
  9. Cleaning the type form.
  10. Distributing the type. 77, 78, 79, 80.

III. Related Information
  1. Mailing sets. 158.
  2. Kinds of announcements. 155, 157.

IV. Judging the Job

QUESTIONS FOR CLASS DISCUSSION

1. What type face is appropriate for a wedding invitation? Fig. 91.

2. What forms may business announcements take? 157.

3. What do you understand about the term "mailing sets"? 158.

4. What kind of stock is usually used in social announcements? 158.

5. What size of type is appropriate for social announcements? 159.

Project Number Five

THE TICKET

I. Layout
   1. Preparing the copy. 114.
   2. Sizes of tickets. 133.
   3. Design. 135.
   4. Fitting the job in type. 110, Fig. 70.
   5. Making the layout. 106, 107, 108, 126.
      a. Display. 89, 90, 91, 92, 94.
      b. Harmony. 95, 96, 97, 98.
      c. Appropriateness. 104.
      d. Choosing the correct type face. 105.
      e. The layout procedure. 109.

II. Operations
   1. Composition
      a. Setting the stick. 40.
      b. Centering a line. 50.
      c. Justifying a line of type. 41.
      d. Setting a border. 87, 135 .
      e. Removing the type from the stick. 66, Fig. 32.
      f. Tying up the type form. 67, Figs. 33, 34.
   2. Pulling a proof. 68.

3. Locking up.   206.
4. Inking the press.   221.
5. Bindery
    a. Figuring the stock.   285, 287.
    b. Cutting the stock.   286.
6. Makeready.   222.
    a. Putting on a new tympan sheet.   222.
    b. Adjusting the impression.   222.
    c. Setting the guides.   223.
7. Feeding the press.   228.
8. Washing the press.   229.
9. Cleaning the type form.
10. Distributing the type.   78, 79, 80.

III. Related Information
    1. Use of tickets.   132.

IV. Judging the Job

QUESTIONS FOR CLASS DISCUSSION

1. Approximately what size are tickets usually printed?   133
2. What stock is used for tickets?   133.
3. What information should be contained in the ticket?   134.
4. How are theater tickets usually manufactured?   132.
5. How should the ticket be composed?   135.

PROJECT NUMBER SIX

THE BOOK PLATE

I. Layout
    1. Preparing the copy.   173.
    2. Sizes of book plates.   174.
    3. Designs.   173, 174, Figs. 100, 101.
    4. Fitting the job in type.   110, Fig. 70.
    5. Making the layout.   106, 107, 108.
        a. Display.   89, 90, 91, 92, 94.

    b. Harmony. 95, 96, 97, 98.

    c. Appropriateness. 104.

    d. Choosing the correct type face. 105.

    e. The layout procedure. 109.

II. Operations

  1. Composition

    a. Setting the stick. 40.

    b. Centering a line. 50.

    c. Justifying a line of type. 41.

    d. Setting a border. 87.

    e. Removing the type from the stick. 66, Fig. 32.

    f. Tying up the type form. 67, Figs. 33, 34.

  2. Pulling a proof. 68.

  3. Locking up. 206.

  4. Inking the press. 221.

  5. Bindery

    a. Figuring the stock. 285, 287.

    b. Cutting the stock. 286.

  6. Makeready. 222.

    a. Putting on a new tympan sheet. 222.

    b. Adjusting the impression. 222.

    c. Setting the guides. 223.

  7. Feeding the press. 228.

  8. Washing the press. 229.

  9. Cleaning the type form.

  10. Distributing the type. 77, 78, 79, 80

III. Related Information

  1. Use of book plates. 172.

  2. History of book plates. 172.

IV. Judging the Job

QUESTIONS FOR CLASS DISCUSSION

1. What copy is usually placed on book plates? 173.

2. In what two ways can a book plate be illustrated? 173.

3. What kind of stock is usually used for book plates? 172.
4. Of what value is the book plate? 172.
5. When and where did book plates originate? 173.

PROJECT NUMBER SEVEN

THE PACKAGE LABEL

I. Layout
1. Preparing the copy. 141.
2. Sizes of package labels. 140.
3. Designs. 159.
4. Fitting the job in type. 110, Fig. 70.
5. Making the layout. 106, 107, 108.
   a. Display. 89, 90, 91, 92, 94.
   b. Harmony. 95, 96, 97, 98.
   c. Appropriateness. 104.
   d. Choosing the correct type face. 105.
   e. The layout procedure. 109.

II. Operations
1. Composition
   a. Setting the stick. 40.
   b. Centering a line. 50.
   c. Justifying a line of type. 41.
   d. Removing the type from the stick. 66, Fig. 32.
   e. Tying up the type form. 67, Figs. 33, 34.
2. Pulling a proof. 68.
3. Locking up. 206.
4. Inking the press. 221.
5. Bindery
   a. Figuring the stock. 285, 287.
   b. Cutting the stock. 286.
6. Makeready. 222.
   a. Putting on a new tympan sheet. 222.
   b. Adjusting the impression. 222.
   c. Setting the guides. 223.

7. Feeding the press. 228.
8. Washing the press. 229.
9. Cleaning the type form.
10. Distributing the type. 78, 79, 80.
III. Related Information
IV. Judging the Job

QUESTIONS FOR CLASS DISCUSSION

1. Of what value are package labels? 140.
2. What kind of paper is usually used for labels? 140.
3. What copy should the label contain? 141
4. What messages to the postmaster may be included in the copy of the label? 141.
5. Why should great care be taken in the printing of package labels? 142.

PROJECT NUMBER EIGHT

THE HANDBILL

I. Layout
1. Preparing the copy. 153.
2. Sizes of handbills. 152.
3. Designs. 154, Fig. 90.
4. Fitting the job in type. 110, Fig. 70.
5. Making the layout. 106, 107, 108.
   a. Display. 89, 90, 91, 92, 94.
   b. Harmony. 95, 96, 97, 98.
   c. Appropriateness. 104.
   d. Choosing the correct type face. 105.
   e. The layout procedure. 109.

II. Operations
1. Composition
   a. Setting the stick. 40.
   b. Centering a line. 50.

      c. Justifying a line of type.   41.

      d. Setting a border.   87.

      e. Removing the type from the stick.   66, Fig. 32.

      f. Tying up the type form.   67, Figs. 33, 34.

  2. Pulling a proof.   68.

  3. Locking up.   206.

  4. Inking the press.   221.

  5. Bindery

      a. Figuring the stock.   285, 287.

      b. Cutting the stock.   286.

  6. Makeready.   222.

      a. Putting on a new tympan sheet.   222.

      b. Adjusting the impression.   222.

      c. Setting the guides.   223.

  7. Feeding the press.   228.

  8. Washing the press.   229.

  9. Cleaning the type form.

  10. Distributing the type.   78, 79, 80.

III. Related Information

IV. Judging the Job

QUESTIONS FOR CLASS DISCUSSION

1. In what three sizes are handbills usually printed? Why? 152.

2. What kind of paper stock is usually used for printing handbills? Why?   152.

3. Why is it necessary for handbill copy to be brief and concise?   153.

4. What style of type is appropriate for the handbill?   154.

5. What width of margins are usually used on 6×9 handbills? 154.

PROJECT NUMBER NINE

THE GREETING CARD

I. Layout
1. Preparing the copy. 161.
2. Sizes of greeting cards. 161.
3. Designs. 160, 161, Figs. 93, 94.
4. Fitting the job in type. 110, Fig. 70
5. Making the layout. 106, 107, 108.
   a. Display. 89, 90, 91, 92, 94.
   b. Harmony. 95, 96, 97, 98.
   c. Appropriateness. 104.
   d. Choosing the correct type face. 105.
   e. The layout procedure. 109.

II. Operations
1. Composition
   a. Setting the stick. 40.
   b. Centering a line. 50.
   c. Justifying a line of type. 41.
   d. Setting a border. 87.
   e. Removing the type from the stick. 66, Fig. 32.
   f. Tying up the type form. 67, Figs. 33, 34.
2. Pulling a proof. 68.
3. Locking up. 206.
4. Inking the press. 221.
5. Bindery
   a. Figuring the stock. 285, 287.
   b. Cutting the stock. 286.
6. Makeready. 222.
   a. Putting on a new tympan sheet. 222.
   b. Adjusting the impression. 222.
   c. Setting the guides. 223.
7. Feeding the press. 228.
8. Washing the press. 229.
9. Cleaning the type form.
10. Distributing the type. 77, 78, 79, 80.

III. Related Information
    1. Use of greeting cards. 160.
    2. History of greeting cards. 160.
    3. Methods of manufacturing greeting cards. 160.

IV. Judging the Job

QUESTIONS FOR CLASS DISCUSSION

1. Of what value are greeting cards? 160.

2. Where did the custom of sending greeting cards originate? 160.

3. Who published the first greeting cards in America? When? 160.

4. By what three methods are greeting cards manufactured? 160.

5. Are greeting cards usually illustrated? By what methods can the student illustrate his personal greeting card? 160.

6. Of what value is the use of mailing sets for greeting cards? 161.

7. How is a size of a greeting card determined? 161.

Project Number Ten

THE POSTER

I. Layout
    1. Preparing the copy. 162, 164.
    2. Sizes of posters and window cards. 163.
    3. Designs. 165.
    4. Fitting the job in type. 110.
    5. Making the layout. 106, 107, 108.
        a. Display. 89, 90, 91, 92, 94.
        b. Harmony. 95, 96, 97, 98.
        c. Appropriateness. 104.
        d. Choosing the correct type face. 105.
        e. The layout procedure. 109.

II. Operations
  1. Composition
     a. Setting the stick. 40.
     b. Centering a line. 50.
     c. Justifying a line of type. 41.
     d. Setting a border. 87.
     e. Removing the type from the stick. 66, Fig. 32.
     f. Tying up the type form. 67, Figs. 33, 34.
  2. Pulling a proof. 68.
  3. Locking up. 206.
  4. Inking the press. 221.
  5. Bindery
     a. Figuring the stock. 285, 287.
     b. Cutting the stock. 286.
  6. Makeready. 222.
     a. Putting on a new tympan sheet. 222.
     b. Adjusting the impression. 222.
     c. Setting the guides. 223.
  7. Feeding the press. 228.
  8. Washing the press. 229.
  9. Cleaning the type form.
  10. Distributing the type. 77, 78, 79, 80.

III. Related Information
  1. Use of posters and window cards. 162.
  2. Kinds of posters. 162, 164, Fig. 96.

IV. Judging the Job

QUESTIONS FOR CLASS DISCUSSION

1. What is the value of a poster? 162.
2. What is the value of a window card? 162.
3. What is the difference in size between the window card and the poster? 163.
4. Why must the copy of a window card be brief? 164.
5. How are interesting quotations printed in school shops? 164.

PROJECT NUMBER ELEVEN

THE PROGRAM

I. Layout
1. Preparing the copy. 148.
2. Sizes of programs. 147.
3. Designs. 149.
4. Fitting the job in type. 110, 151, Fig. 70.
5. Making the layout. 106, 107, 108, Fig. 89.
    a. Display. 89, 90, 91, 92, 94.
    b. Harmony. 95, 96, 97, 98.
    c. Appropriateness. 104.
    d. Choosing the correct type face. 105.
    e. The layout procedure. 109.

II. Operations
1. Composition
    a. Setting the stick. 40.
    b. Centering a line. 50.
    c. Justifying a line of type. 41.
    d. Use of leaders. 61, 151.
    e. Removing the type from the stick. 66, Fig. 32.
    f. Tying up the type form. 67, Figs. 33, 34.
2. Pulling a proof. 68.
3. Locking up. 206.
4. Inking the press. 221.
5. Bindery
    a. Figuring the stock. 285, 287.
    b. Cutting the stock. 286.
6. Makeready. 222.
    a. Putting on a new tympan sheet. 222.
    b. Adjusting the impression. 222.
    c. Setting the guides. 223.
7. Feeding the press. 228.
8. Washing the press. 229.
9. Cleaning the type form.
10. Distributing the type. 77, 78, 79, 80.

III. Related Information
    1. Use of programs. 147.
    2. Appropriate types for programs. 149.
    3. Dance programs. 150.
IV. Judging the Job

QUESTIONS FOR CLASS DISCUSSION

1. Of what use are programs? 147.
2. What copy does the program contain? 148.
3. What type would be appropriate for church programs? 149.
4. Discuss the use of leaders in programs. 151.
5. In what forms are programs printed? 147.

SUGGESTED PROJECTS

After having produced many of the projects in this booklet, most pupils without doubt will have many ideas of their own for projects. However, in the event that a pupil has completed the projects as outlined and does not yet understand the time saving and valuable use of printing, the following projects may give him ideas on which to work.

THE MEMBERSHIP CARD

Most boys belong to one or more clubs or organizations which may very profitably issue membership cards to members.

THE TAG

Tags are quite handy for the shipping of packages, boxes and bundles. As illustrated and treated in detail in the text in paragraphs 136 to 139, the tag is a useful project.

Tags may also be printed square, punched in one corner and a string attached to the lapel button hole to advertise and serve as an admission ticket for athletic games and school plays. Tags may easily be made from a tough cardboard on the press by die-cutting them in the desired shape with steel rule.

THE BOOK MARK

Scrap stock of all kinds of cardboard, even if only one inch wide, may be utilized for the printing of book marks. They may also be printed to advertise books in the school library or various school activities.

THE STICKER

Stickers printed in the form of flags, circles, ovals, or any other desired shape may easily be printed from linoleum blocks on gummed paper. Printed on the gummed side, they are useful for automobile windshields. Stickers printed on the ungummed side are popular for showing school colors and school names on books, suitcases, and the like.

THE SCHEDULE CARD

Many boys have added to their popularity by printing class schedule cards for their home room class.

Schedules for basket ball or football games are also very handy.

THE CALENDAR

Many school shops, just before Christmas, print calendars either for pupil use or to sell to pupils in the school. A picture of the school building on a small flat wall calendar, and the desk type, cut with steel rule to stand upright on a desk, are quite popular.

MULE BAROMETER

The idea of a mule barometer is old, but ever popular. The tail is made from a piece of rope knotted on the back of the card, and brought through by punching a hole.

PADDED PROJECTS

Very handy and useful projects, if binding equipment is provided, are the tally, "500" and bridge score pads, memorandum and phone call pads or booklets. Ideas may be gathered from samples seen in stationery stores, and the form imprinted with the name of the student or the school.

OBJECTIVE TESTS

FOR USE WITH
"PRINTING AND THE ALLIED TRADES"

INSTRUCTIONS

1. Do not write in the book—write on the test card provided.

2. Questions are in the following forms: "multiple choice" questions, "true or false" statements, and questions requiring "short answers."

SUGGESTED CARD FORM FOR EXAMINATIONS OR STUDENT SELF-TESTING

TEST CARD

Chapter............   Name.................................
Date...............   Grade........   Mark..............

1	14
2	15
3	16
4	17
5	18
6	19
7	20
8	21
9	22
10	23
11	24
12	25
13	26

3. In statements that are either true or false, mark **T** in the space provided after the question number on the card. If false, mark an **F**.

4. In multiple choice forms, select from the list of statements the most logical answer or answers and mark its number or their numbers in the space provided on the card.

5. In short answer questions, use only one word or figure on the card.

The Objective Test Grading Table may be used by those who desire to transpose their marks into per cents. In this table, per cents are carried only to two places.

Chapter I

1. The first printer using movable type is credited to: **1.**
   1. Gutenberg.   4. Bodoni.
   2. The Chinese.   5. Kennerley.
   3. Caxton.

2. The first printing from movable type was done in Europe about the year: **4.**
   1. 1650.   4. 1350.
   2. 1450.   5. 1250.
   3. 1750.

3. The first European printer was: **5.**
   1. Caxton.   8. Sweynheym.
   2. Pannartz.   9. Jenson.
   3. Gutenberg.   10. Aldus Manutius.
   4. Gering.   11. Freiburger.
   5. Kranz.   12. Daye.
   6. Fust.   13. Green.
   7. Schoeffer.

4. The men associated with the first European printer were: **5.** (See list of answers in question 3.)

OBJECTIVE TEST GRADING TABLE

Total Number of Questions Answered Correctly in Nearest Even Percents of the Total

No. of Questions in Test	26	25	24	23	22	21	20	19	18	17	16	15	14	13	12	11	10	9	8	7	6	5	4	3	2	1	0
5																						100	80	60	40	20	0
6																					100	83	67	50	33	17	0
7																				100	86	71	57	43	28	14	0
10																	100	90	80	70	60	50	40	30	20	10	0
11																100	90	82	73	64	55	45	36	27	18	10	0
12															100	92	83	75	67	58	50	42	33	25	17	8	0
13														100	92	85	77	69	62	54	46	38	31	23	15	8	0
15												100	93	87	80	73	67	60	53	47	40	33	27	20	13	7	0
16											100	94	87	81	75	69	62	56	50	44	37	31	25	19	12	6	0
19								100	95	89	84	79	74	68	63	58	53	47	42	37	32	26	21	16	11	5	0
21						100	95	91	86	81	76	71	67	62	57	52	48	43	38	33	29	24	19	14	10	5	0
22					100	95	91	86	82	77	73	68	64	59	54	50	45	41	36	32	27	23	18	14	9	5	0
23				100	96	91	87	83	78	74	70	65	61	57	52	48	43	39	35	30	26	22	17	13	9	4	0
24			100	96	92	87	83	79	75	71	67	62	58	54	50	46	42	37	33	29	25	21	17	12	8	4	0
26	100	96	92	88	85	81	77	73	69	65	62	58	54	50	46	42	38	35	31	27	23	19	15	12	8	4	0

5. The first two printers in Italy were: 7.
(See list of answers in question 3.)

6. The man first to use pure roman-faced type was: 7.
(See list of answers in question 3.)

7. The designer of the italic type was: 7.
(See list of answers in question 3.)

8. The three first printers in France were: 8.
(See list of answers in question 3.)

9. The first English printer was: 9.
(See list of answers in question 3.)

10. The first British-American printer was: 10.
(See list of answers in question 3.)

11. The first man to print a newspaper in America was: 10.
(See list of answers in question 3.)

12. The first printings in Europe were: 4.
    1. Indulgences.
    2. Bibles.
    3. Books.
    4. Prints of religious character.
    5. Block books.

CHAPTER II

1. Modern printing, as we know it today, probably was in practical use about: 11.
    1. 1740.   4. 1540.
    2. 1840.   5. 1440.
    3. 1640.

2. The most important of the printing processes is: 13.
    1. Letterpress.
    2. Lithography (offset).
    3. Intaglio (gravure).

3. The three departments of a print shop are: 13.

4. Printing establishments in the United States number about: 12.
   1. 23,500.   4. 53,500.
   2. 32,500.   5. 15,500.
   3. 43,500.

5. In the number of establishments, printing ranks: 12.
   1. First.   4. Fourth.   13. Thirteenth.
   2. Second.   5. Fifth.   15. Fifteenth.
   3. Third.   6. Sixth.

6. In added value by manufacture, printing ranks: 12.
   (See list of answers under question 5.)

7. In wages paid, printing ranks: 12.
   (See list of answers under question 5.)

8. In value of products, printing ranks: 12.
   (See list of answers under question 5.)

9. In number of wage earners, printing ranks: 12.
   (See list of answers under question 5.)

10. Printing from raised surfaces is known as: 13.
    1. Letterpress.   3. Intaglio.
    2. Lithography.   4. Silk screen.

11. Printing from plane surfaces is known as: 13.
    (See list of answers under question 10.)

12. Printing from depressions in a plate is known as: 13.
    (See list of answers under question 10.)

13. Printing through a stencil is known as: 13a.
    (See list of answers under question 10.)

Chapter III

1. Type is made of three ingredients: 16.
   1. Brass.   4. Tin.   7. Silver.
   2. Lead.   5. Iron.   8. Antimony.
   3. Zinc.   6. Steel.   9. Platinum.

2. The square of the type body of any one size is called the: 34.
    1. En quad.
    2. Em quad.
    3. Point.
    4. 3-em space.
    5. Nut quad.

3. The shoulder of a piece of type is the: 17.
    1. The top of the type below the face.
    2. Cross lines at the ends of the main strokes.
    3. The beveled space below the face.
    4. The projections on which the type stands.
    5. Guides to the compositor in setting type.

4. Types may be classified into the following main divisions: 19.
    1. Bold, text, condensed, script.
    2. Shaded, Gothic, text, italic.
    3. Roman, Gothic, italic, text, script.
    4. Initial letters, outline, shaded.
    5. Roman, Gothic, text, script.

5. One inch is equal to: 22.
    1. 6 picas.
    2. 10 picas.
    3. 3 picas.
    4. 4 picas.
    5. 7 picas.

6. The nonpareil is equal to: 22.
    1. 36 points.   3. 12 points.   4. 6 points.
    2. 72 points.   5. 1 point.

7. One family of type is made up of: 21.
    1. Caslon Bold, Caslon Italic, Caslon 540, Caslon Condensed.
    2. Invitation Text in sizes 6-point to 72-point.
    3. Century Light, Caslon Light, Cheltenham Light.
    4. Text, Script, Bold, Italic.

8. Which of the following cases is more generally used?   28.
    1. Two-thirds.
    2. News.
    3. Yankee.
    4. Triple.
    5. California.

9. The height-to-paper of type in the United States is: 15.
   1. .928   4. .981
   2. .917   5. .819
   3. .918

10. The serifs of a piece of type are: 17.
    1. The top of the type below the face.
    2. Cross lines at the ends of the main strokes.
    3. The beveled space below the face.
    4. The projections on which the type stands.
    5. Guides to the compositor in setting type.

11. Nicks on type: 17.
    1. Distinguish between fonts on all kinds of type faces.
    2. Act as a guide to the compositor.
    3. Are the ejecting marks of the type caster.
    4. Are the marks formed by the tool that removes the jet.
    5. Are the cross lines at the ends of the main strokes.

12. A kern is: 17.
    1. A cross line at the ends of the main strokes.
    2. The top of the type below the face.
    3. The projection on which the type stands.
    4. That part of the face that extends over the side of the body.
    5. A guide to the compositor.

13. Ligatures are used to: 18.
    1. Save time in composition.
    2. Print straight lines.
    3. Print dotted lines.
    4. Form the skeleton of a form.
    5. Prevent kerned letters from breaking.

14. Type series in foundry type usually run: 26.
    1. 6, 8, 10, 12, 14, 17, 18, 20.
    2. 6, 8, 10, 12, 14, 18, 26, 30.
    3. 6, 8, 10, 12, 14, 18, 24, 36.
    4. 6, 8, 10, 12, 14, 18, 23, 36.
    5. 8, 10, 12, 14, 16, 18, 20, 24.

15. Which of the following capital letters is not in alphabetical order in the California job case?　Fig. 10.

   1. H　　　　　　　　3. L　　　　　　　　4. V
   2. U　　　　　　　　　　　　　　　　　　　5. G

16. The printer measures type matter with a:　Fig. 8.

   1. Brass rule.　　　　　　　　4. Linear ruler.
   2. Reglet.　　　　　　　　　　5. String.
   3. Line gauge.

17. A font is:　18.

   1. A part of the type face.
   2. A ligature.
   3. A kind of type face.
   4. An assortment of type.
   5. A unit of measure.

18. Old style type has:　20.

   1. Regularity of shape.
   2. Diagonally sloping serifs.
   3. No serifs.
   4. Accurate curves.
   5. Height equal to width.

19. Modern type has:　20.

   1. Regularity of shape.
   2. Diagonally sloping serifs.
   3. No serifs.
   4. Inaccurate curves.
   5. Height equal to width.

CHAPTER IV

1. Labor saving leads and slugs are cut to point lengths.　31.

2. When necessary to piece leads or slugs of 20 picas wide, two 10-pica pieces are used.　32.

3. Leads are made in one- and two-point widths.　31.

4. The em quad is the square of any size of type. 34.

5. The 3-em space is one-third of an em quad. 34.

6. The 4-em space is one-fourth of an em quad. 34.

7. The 5-em space is one-fifth of an em quad. 34.

8. A two-em quad is twice the width of the em quad. 34.

9. A nonpareil reglet is 12 points thick. 35.

10. A pica reglet is 6 points thick. 35.

11. Reglet is used for locking up type forms for the press. 35.

12. Furniture is made of both metal and wood. 36.

13. Solid matter is type set with leads between lines. 31.

14. An 18-point 3-em space is identical in size to the 6-point 3-em quad.

15. A 24-point 2-em quad is identical in size to the 42-point en quad.

16. A 12-point 3-em space is identical in size to the 36-point en quad.

17. An 8-point 3-em quad is identical in size to the 24-point 3-em space.

18. There are four 6-point em quads in a 12-point em quad.

19. There are nine 6-point em quads in an 18-point em quad.

20. There are twelve 6-point em quads in a 24-point em quad.

21. Twenty-four picas are the same as: 34.
    1. 50 nonpareils.
    2. 48 points.
    3. 24 ems.
    4. 188 points.
    5. One inch.

22. The printer's basic unit of measure is called the: 34.
    1. Nonpareil.   4. Quad.
    2. Lead.   5. Pica.
    3. Inch.

23. The pica is equal to:
    1. 6 points.   4. 10 points.
    2. 3 nonpareils.   5. 20 points.
    3. 12 points.

Chapter V

1. Plain composition consists of: 38.
    1. Ordinary paragraph matter.
    2. The setting of large types in ads, letterheads, envelopes, etc.
    3. The centering of lines of small type.
    4. Setting plain types.

2. Display composition consists of: 89, 90.
   (See list of above answers.)

3. Composing sticks can usually be set to: 39.
    1. Inches.
    2. Picas and points.
    3. Picas only.
    4. Six-point graduations.

4. Justification consists of: 41.
    1. Centering lines of type.
    2. Adjusting spaces equally between words.
    3. Making each line of type the same width.
    4. Setting straight or display composition.

5. The term "spacing" consists of: 42.
   (See list of above answers.)

6. The space or quad placed between words in first setting a line of type is the: 34.
  1. En quad.   4. 5-em space.
  2. Em quad.   5. 3-em space.
  3. 4-em space.

7. In quadding out at the ends of lines in setting type, the following is done: 47.
  1. Smallest space is placed at the end of the line.
  2. Largest quad is placed at the end of the line, with all small spaces between them.
  3. Spaces and quads are arranged so that the largest is placed at the end of the line, and smallest nearer the type.
  4. There is no set procedure for this.

8. Type is read: 48.
  1. From left to right, nick-side up.
  2. From left to right, nick-side down.
  3. Nick up from right to left.
  4. Nick down.

9. Beginning quotation marks are usually made by: 52.
  1. Turning two apostrophes nick up.
  2. Turning two apostrophes nick down.
  3. Turning two commas nick up.
  4. Turning two commas nick down.

10. In setting all cap letters, it is better to have between words: 53.
  1. A 3-em space.
  2. An en quad.
  3. An em quad.
  4. Two 3-em spaces.

11. Roman numerals are made up of: 63.
  1. Caps.
  2. Lowercase.
  3. Small caps.

12. Ditto marks are made up of: 64.
    1. Commas turned nick up.
    2. Commas turned nick down.
    3. Apostrophes turned nick up.
    4. Apostrophes turned nick down.

13. Roman type can be either: 19.
    1. Bold face and light face.
    2. Italic and bold face.
    3. Light and italic.
    4. Bold and text.
    5. Text and light face.

14. Leads are, in usual practice, of the following thickness: 31.
    1. Six points.   4. Twelve points.
    2. Four points.   5. Three points.
    3. Two points.

15. Thicknesses of spaces and quads and their combinations are in this order, from smallest to largest: 43, 44.
    1. 5-em, 3-em, 4-em, two 4-ems, en, 3-em and 4-em, en and 3-em.
    2. 5-em, 4-em, two 5-ems, en, 3-em and 4-em, two 3-ems, 3-em and em.
    3. 5-em, 4-em, two 5-ems, 5-em and 4-em, en, 3-em and 4-em, two 3-ems, 3-em and nut.
    4. 3-em, 4-em, 5-em, en, two 3-ems, 3-em and en.
    5. 4-em, 3-em, 5-em, en, em.

16. The term "justification" is applied to: 41.
    1. Making a line fit a given measure.
    2. Setting spaces between lines of type.
    3. Setting the correct space between words.
    4. Quadding out type lines.
    5. Preparing a form for the press.

18. The first step in decreasing space between words is to substitute: 43.
    1. 4-em spaces.   4. Two 3-em spaces.
    2. En quads.   5. Two 4-em spaces.
    3. 5-em spaces.

19. The second step in decreasing space between words is: (Use the choices listed under question 18.) 43.

20. The first step in increasing space between words is: **44.**
    1. Substitute 4-em spaces.
    2. Substitute en quads.
    3. Substitute 5-em spaces.
    4. Substitute two 3-em spaces.
    5. Substitute 4-em space and 3-em space.

21. The second step in increasing space between words is: **44.** (Use the choices listed under question 20.)

22. The third step in increasing space between words is: **44.** (Use choices listed under question 20.)

23. The best procedure in centering a line is: 50.
    1. Measure with a rule to find the center.
    2. Guess at the center.
    3. Count the quads and spaces on each side of the line
    4. Approximate the center and then fill in with quads.
    5. Measure for the center and then fill in with quads.

24. In quadding out lines: 47.
    1. Em quads are used with spaces between words.
    2. Two-em quads are used with necessary spaces.
    3. The largest quads possible are used, with any necessary smaller spaces placed at the ends of the lines.
    4. Three-em quads are used exclusively.
    5. The largest quads possible are used, with any necessary spaces placed between the last words in the line and the first quad.

25. Letterspacing is resorted to only when it improves the appearance of the form. 60.

26. Leaders are made in en, em, 2-em and 3-em sizes. 61.

CHAPTER VI

1. A brayer is: 68.
    1. A type receptable.
    2. A storage case.
    3. An inking roller.
    4. A printing machine.

2. The easiest method of taking a proof of a book page is: 68.
    1. On imposing table.
    2. On a printing press.
    3. On a galley.
    4. On a proof press.
    5. In a chase.

3. A copy holder: 71.
    1. Edits copy.
    2. Cuts copy.
    3. Reads copy.
    4. Marks proof.
    5. Takes proof.

4. A "revise" is a: 75.
    1. Proofreader's helper.
    2. First proof.
    3. Second proof.
    4. Proofreader's mark.

5. Type forms are tied with string so that: 67.
    1. Only one end is left protruding from the wrapping.
    2. With the use of a knot.
    3. Loosely with string.
    4. Securely with furniture.

6. The proofreader's mark for delete (take out) is: Fig. 37.

7. The proofreader's mark for pushing down space is: Fig. 37.

8. The proofreader's mark for turning over a letter is: Fig. 37.

9. The proofreader's mark for a defective letter is: Fig. 37.

10. The proofreader's mark for inserting a space is: Fig. 37.

11. The proofreader's mark for closing up space is: Fig. 37.

12. The proofreader's mark for inserting a period is: Fig. 37.

13. The proofreader's mark for inserting a comma is: Fig. 37.

14. The proofreader's mark for inserting a colon is: Fig. 37.

15. The proofreader's mark for inserting a hyphen is: Fig. 37.

16. The proofreader's mark for moving left is: Fig. 37.

17. The proofreader's mark for moving right is: Fig. 37.

18. The proofreader's mark for wrong font letters is: Fig. 37.

19. List the duties of a proofreader briefly: Fig. 37.

Chapter VII

1. Distribution means the placing of type and materials back into their respective cases or racks.   76.

2. The term distribution also includes the breaking up of machine set matter.   78a.

3. The conceded best practice in distributing leads and slugs is to: 80.
    1. Place them back in the rack one by one as found in the distribution.
    2. Pick them from the material indiscriminately.
    3. Measure them and place them back one by one.
    4. Stand them first in a galley and arrange them in sizes for distribution.
    5. Stand them on the bank.

4. Type matter ready to go to press is called: 76.
    1. Straight matter.
    2. Dead matter.
    3. Live matter.
    4. Spacing material.
    5. Copy material.

5. In general practice, small forms of straight matter or display lines are distributed directly from: 77.
   1. The imposing table.
   2. A galley.
   3. The hand.
   4. The chase.
   5. The stick.

6. To prevent mixing type fonts in distribution: 79.
   1. The faces and nicks should be compared.
   2. The compositor should ask the foreman.
   3. Nicks should be compared.
   4. Faces should be compared.
   5. Serifs should be compared.

7. The "non-distribution system" is that in which all matter is thrown into the melting furnace.   78a.

Chapter VIII

1. Brass rule, in general practice: 85.
   1. Is less durable than machine rule.
   2. Is more easily cut than machine rule.
   3. Has both top and bottom prepared as a printing sur-face.
   4. Is cut to size on a saw-trimmer.
   5. Is usually made in the shop.

2. Linotype border is made in: 86.
   1. 24-inch strips.
   2. Single units of border.
   3. 30- or 42-pica strips.
   4. Any size.
   5. 6-inch strips.

3. Unit monotype borders are made in: 83.
   1. 24-inch strips.
   2. Single units.

    3. 30- or 42-pica strips.
    4. Any size.
    5. 6-inch strips.

4. The best way to miter rules and line borders is to: 83.
    1. Use a rotary miterer.
    2. Use a hand miterer.
    3. Use a saw trimmer.
    4. Cut them by hand.
    5. Cut them on a slug cutter.

5. Linotype border is often made with corner pieces. Fig. 42.

Chapter IX

1. A line of type may be displayed by: **90.**
    1. Contrast in sizes.
    2. Contrast in shape.
    3. Printing heavier on the paper.
    4. Isolating a line or word.
    5. By printing in a different color.

2. Forms of display consist of: 94.
    1. Balanced long and short lines.
    2. Half-diamond indention.
    3. Squared indention.
    4. Printing with a heavy impression on the paper.
    5. Mixing type families.

3. Display of minor copy lines is done by: 91.
    1. Setting them in caps.
    2. Printing with heavier impression on paper.
    3. Setting them in small caps.
    4. Setting them in caps.
    5. Setting them in italics.

4. It is necessary to display the right lines of type in order to: 89.
   1. Make the job "look" right.
   2. Attract general attention.
   3. Direct attention to the advertised product or price.
   4. Make the job easier to set.
   5. Satisfy the customer.

5. The type that harmonizes best with Caslon Oldstyle is: 96.
   1. Cheltenham bold.
   2. Cheltenham medium.
   3. Gothic.
   4. Caslon bold.
   5. Text.

6. The type that harmonizes best with Cheltenham Bold Extended is: 96.
   1. Gothic extended.
   2. Caslon italic.
   3. Cheltenham bold.
   4. Engravers bold.
   5. Caslon condensed.

7. The type that harmonizes best with Bodoni Bold is: 96.
   1. Cheltenham light.
   2. Caslon Oldstyle.
   3. Bodoni book.
   4. Script.
   5. Engravers bold.

8. Harmony of tone in display composition exists where: 97.
   1. Thin types are used in thin set-ups.
   2. Type faces, border and ornament are of the same shape.
   3. Type faces, border and ornament are of the same degree of density.
   4. Wide types are set in wide set-ups.
   5. One series of type is used in the same set-up.

9. Harmony of shape in display composition exists where: 98.
    1. Parts of a job are set in the same type face.
    2. Parts of a job are similar in shape.
    3. Parts of a job are dissimilar in shape.
    4. Parts of a job are set in contrasting type faces.
    5. Parts of a job are equal.

10. The optical center of a rectangle appears: 99.
    1. Slightly lower than the mathematical center.
    2. Slightly higher than the mathematical center.
    3. At the mathematical center.
    4. Three-quarters from the top.
    5. Three-quarters from the bottom.

11. Balance, in display composition, concerns: **100.**
    1. The forming of margins.
    2. The laying out of the job.
    3. The equalizing of the parts of a job.
    4. The centering of lines.
    5. The correct spacing of the line.

12. An appropriate type face for a hardware advertisement is:
    1. Script.   4. Text.
    2. Bold face.   5. Light face.
    3. Shaded.

13. An appropriate type face for a hairdresser's announcement is:
    104.
    1. Bold face.   4. Condensed.
    2. Bold text.   5. Italic.
    3. Extended.

14. An appropriate type face for a banker's letterhead is: 104.
    1. Caslon bold.
    2. Steelplate Gothic.
    3. Script.
    4. Condensed caslon bold.
    5. Extended caslon bold.

15. A dummy is a: 111.
    1. Layout for an advertisement.
    2. Layout for a title page.
    3. Layout for a book, pamphlet, or folder.
    4. Layout for a letterhead.
    5. Layout for a series of small jobs.

16. "Bleeding" means to run the illustrations of a piece of printing into the margin: 102.

17. A layout is a working plan for a piece of printing.   106.

18. A layout is made to: 107.
    1. Give the student something to do.
    2. Give a general idea of how the job will look in type.
    3. Help the pressman.
    4. Make work for more men.

19. The unit count is better than the general table of words to the square inch in fitting body matter.   113.

Chapter X

1. The most used envelope size is the: 115.
    1. No. $6\frac{3}{4}$.   4. No. 10.
    2. No. 7.   5. No. 12.
    3. No. 9.

2. Envelope corner cards do not usually have the main display line set larger than: 117.
    1. 6-point.   4. 12-point.
    2. 8-point.   5. 14-point.
    3. 10-point.

3. The most usual letterhead size is the: 118.
    1. $5\frac{1}{2}\times8\frac{1}{2}$ inch size.
    2. $8\frac{1}{2}\times11$ inch size.
    3. 8×10 inch size.
    4. $7\times10\frac{1}{2}$ inch size.
    5. $7\frac{1}{4}\times10\frac{1}{2}$ inch size.

4. In general practice, the main display line of a business card is set in the: 126.
    1. Mathematical center of the card.
    2. At the top.
    3. At the optical center.
    4. Near the top.
    5. Elsewhere on the card.

5. Cards for men are usually printed upon a size about: Fig. 79.
    1. $3\frac{1}{4} \times 1\frac{1}{2}$.   4. 1×2.
    2. 3×2.   5. 2×4.
    3. $3\frac{1}{4} \times 2\frac{1}{4}$.

6. Cards for young unmarried women are usually printed upon a size about: Fig. 79.
(See list of answers in question 5.)

7. Cards for married women are usually printed upon a size about: Fig. 79.
(See list of answers in question 5.)

8. When composing an admission ticket, list in order the preference in display of lines: 134.
    1. Price of admission.
    2. Day, month and year and time.
    3. Place.
    4. Organization giving presentation.
    5. Title of presentation.

9. Package labels are usually printed 6×4 inches. 140.

10. The words "To" and "From" must always appear on a tag. 139.

11. There is no set style for menus. 144.

12. Handbills are usually printed in the 6×9 inch size. 152.
When the newspaper column is 12 picas wide:

13. A two column ad is set how many picas wide? 167.

14. A three column ad is set how many picas wide? 167.

15. A four column ad is set how many picas wide? 167.

16. A five column ad is set how many picas wide? 167.

17. A six column ad is set how many picas wide? 167.

18. A seven column ad is set how many picas wide? 167.

19. An eight column ad is set how many picas wide? 167.

20. An agate line is of the following size: 167.
　　1. 5 points.　　　　　　　4. 4 points.
　　2. 5½ points.　　　　　　5. 4½ points.
　　3. 6 points.

21. A "column rule" is used: 167.
　　1. Between ads.
　　2. Between columns.
　　3. Between ads and text matter.
　　4. At the bottom of columns.

22. A "cut off rule" is used: 168.
　　(See answers in question 21.)

23. A "work-and-twist" form is printed on stock cut double, and two impressions are set head-to-head and printed. 177.

CHAPTER XI

1. The Ludlow is especially adapted to casting: 189.
　　1. Straight matter composition.
　　2. Single types for the case.
　　3. Leads, slugs, and line borders.
　　4. Single unit borders.
　　5. Larger sizes of display type.
　　6. Large type for the cases.

2. The Monotype material maker is especially adapted to casting: 198.
　　(See list of answers under question 1.)

3. The Monotype composition machine is especially adapted to casting: 197.
(See list of answers under question **1**.)

4. The Monotype Type and Rule caster is especially adapted to casting: 199.
(See list of answers under question **1**.)

5. The Monotype Giant caster is especially adapted to casting: 200.
(See list of answers under question **1**.)

6. The All-Purpose Linotype is especially adapted to casting: 187.
(See list of answers under question **1**.)

7. The Elrod is especially adapted to casting: 191.
(See list of answers under question **1**.)

8. Errors are corrected on the linotype and intertype by: 184.
    1. Hand, as in hand composition.
    2. Casting a complete new line.
    3. Resetting all or part of a line.
    4. Making a new form.
    5. The use of tweezers.

9. Errors are corrected on the monotype by: 197.
(See list of answers under question **8**.)

10. Errors are corrected on the Ludlow and All-Purpose Linotype by: 187, 190.
(See list of answers under question **8**.)

11. Spacebands are used between words on a: 182.
    1. Monotype.   4. Ludlow.
    2. Linotype   5. A-P-L.
    3. Elrod.

12. The only machines that produce unbreakable full-kerning lines of type from slanting matrices are the: 187, 190.
    1. Linotype.   4. Monotype.
    2. Ludlow.   5. Linograph.
    3. Intertype.   6. A-P-L.

13. Display faces of large type are cast with an overhang, like the letter T, on the: 190.
(See list of answers under question 12.)

14. Strip material in long lengths is cast on the: 198.
(See list of answers under question 12.)

15. The machine that sets type in one measure of 65 picas is the: 197.
(See list of answers under question 12.)

16. The only composing system that sets justified lines of small type, casts low leads and slugs, makes unit borders and metal furniture is the: 196.
(See list of answers under question 12.)

17. Lines longer than 30 or 42 picas, cast on the slugcasting machines, can be used by "butting" the slugs: 183.

18. Roman, italic, small caps and bold face can be set on the following machine from one font of matrices: 197.
     1. Monotype composition machine.
     2. Monotype Giant caster.
     3. Intertype.
     4. Ludlow.
     5. Linotype.

19. The Monotype keyboard contains five alphabets.   194.

20. The Teletypesetter is a device for casting slugs automatically on a line-casting machine.   188.

21. The Monotype ribbon is run backwards through the composing machine.   195.

22. The basic letter of the Monotype font, the M, is divided into the following number of units: 195.
     1. Nine.   3. Sixteen.   5. Eighteen.
     2. Ten.   4. Twenty.

23. The following firms rent matrices to printing firms: **197.**
    1. Monotype.   4. Ludlow.
    2. Intertype.   5. Linograph.
    3. Linotype.

24. The Monotype-Thompson Typecaster can make single **types** from the matrices of any other machine.   200a.

25. Matrices may be set by hand on the Linotype and Intertype. 185.

26. Some linecasting machines automatically quad out the lines. 186.

Chapter XII

1. A chase consists of: 202.
    1. Small iron tools which act as wedges in locking forms.
    2. An iron or steel frame which holds forms in position on a press.
    3. Spacing material used in locking forms in a press.
    4. Nonpareil and pica lengths of spacing material used in locking forms for the press.
    5. A block used to knock type in a form to its feet.
    6. A flat surface on which forms are locked for the press.

2. A planer consists of: 205.
  (See answers under question 1.)

3. Reglet consists of: 204.
  (See answers under question 1.)

4. Quoins are: 203.
  (See answers under question 1.)

5. Furniture consists of: 204.
  (See answers under question 1.)

6. An imposing table consists of: 201.
  (See answers under question 1.)

7. The term "imposition" means: 208.
    1. Locking up a form.
    2. Proofing on the imposing table.
    3. The proper placing of two or more pages.
    4. Breaking up a form.
    5. Locking up large single page forms.

8. What is a work-and-turn form?   209.
    1. A form backed up with the same form.
    2. Book form, printed on one side of paper only, another form being printed on the other side.
    3. Printed, then turned end-for-end and backed up with another form.
    4. Rule form, with crossed lines, printed in two impressions.
    5. A two-color form.

9. What is a sheet-wise form?   209.
(Use choices listed with question 8.)

10. The term "folio" is applied to: 215.
    1. A kind of paper.
    2. Sizes of chase.
    3. Kinds of chases.
    4. Positioning in the chase.
    5. Page numbers.

11. A form is locked tight before planing.   206.

12. When a form is said to "lift," it means that the type matter is held securely.   206.

13. Allowance for trim of the book must be made in imposition. 216.

Chapter XIII

1. List the three basic types of printing presses.   217.

2. The automatic device for feeding ink to the press is called the: 219.

    1. Feed board.   4. Rollers.

    2. Ink disc.   5. Bed.

    3. Fountain.

3. The device used to keep a sheet from being printed on a platen press, while the press continues to run, is called the: 219.

    1. Grippers.   4. Throw-off lever.

    2. Treadle.   5. Fountain.

    3. Platen.

4. What is the chase pressed against when the press is in operation? 219.

    1. Bed.   4. Grippers.

    2. Platen.   5. Rollers.

    3. Tympan.

5. With what is the tympan fastened to the platen? 219.

    1. Grippers.   4. Disc.

    2. Bales.   5. Platens.

    3. Chases.

6. Two ingredients used in making composition rollers are: 220.

    1. Glue and rubber.

    2. Glycerine and glue.

    3. Molasses and rubber.

    4. Raw rubber and glucose.

    5. Glucose and glue.

7. One make of the sliding platen, or rigid bed platen press is the: 218.

    1. Colt's Armory.

    2. Chandler and Price.

    3. Kelly.

    4. Lee.

    5. Miehle.

8. One make of the clam shell press is the: 218.
  (See list of answers under question 7.)

9. One make of two-revolution press is the: Figs. 138, 139.
  1. Web.
  2. Kelly.
  3. Colt's Armory.
  4. Perfecting.
  5. Drum Cylinder.

10. One make of rotary press is the: Fig. 143.
  1. Harris.
  2. Kluge.
  3. Miller.
  4. Miehle Vertical.
  5. Kelly.

11. Guides used on a platen press: 223.
  1. Hold the tympan in place.
  2. Adjust the impression.
  3. Hold the sheet in place.
  4. Aid in picking up the sheet.
  5. Grip the sheet.

12. The underlay, in makeready, is used: 224.
  1. Pasted on top of the tympan sheet.
  2. Pasted to the under side of the tympan sheet.
  3. Pasted to the tympan undersheet.
  4. Between electrotype and block.
  5. Pasted behind the form.

13. What kind of paper is usually used in filling out an overlay?
  225.
  1. Bond.
  2. News.
  3. French folio.
  4. S. & S. C.
  5. M. F.

14. The interlay, in makeready, is used: 226.
  (See list of answers under question 13.)

15. The overlay, in makeready, is used: 225.
  (See list of answers under question 13.)

16. Platen presses, using regular printing ink, are usually washed
  with: 229.

17. Platen press guides are often made with quads. 223.

18. A tympan sheet is used on the top of the platen press packing. 222.

19. The drum cylinder makes one revolution when printing a sheet· 232.

20. Rotary presses print from curved plates. 236.

21. Newspaper presses are divided into units, each of which can be operated independently of the others. 236.

22. Non-offset guns eliminate the smudging of ink on paper as it comes from the press. 238a.

CHAPTER XIV

1. List the three types of plates made by the photo-engraving process. 239.

2. Line etching duplicate half shades of tone. 240.

3. Dragon's blood is used in making line-plates only.

4. Plates for printing on news stock should have the following screen: 242.
    1. 50 to 85 line.
    2. 100 to 133 line.
    3. 120 to 150 line.
    4. 150 to 175 line.
    5. 85 to 100 line.

5. Plates for printing on bond stock should have the following screen: 242.
   (See list of answers under question 4.)

6. Plates for printing on machine finish and s. & s.c. should have the following screen: 242.
   (See list of answers under question 4.)

7. Plates for printing on dull finish coated book stock should have the following screen: 242.
   (See list of answers under question 4.)

8. Plates for printing on enameled stocks should have the following screen: 242.
   (See list of answers under question 4.)

9. The Ben Day Process is a: 244.
   1. Coloring process.
   2. Shading process.
   3. Enlarging process.
   4. Reducing process.
   5. Printing process.

10. A halftone duplicates: 241.
    1. Black lines only.
    2. Medium tones.
    3. White.
    4. Colors.
    5. Shades of color.

11. A halftone is made up of thousands of tiny dots. 242.

12. Wood engravings are still used to illustrate such work as jewelry. 245.

13. Linoleum blocks are the easiest way in which to illustrate. 246.

14. Pictures may be rolled to send to the photo-engraver. 243.

15. Directions should never be written on the back of a photograph being sent to the photo-engraver. 243.

16. Rubber block printing plates have a better printing surface than linoleum plates. 246a.

Chapter XV

1. List four advantages in the use of electrotypes and stereotypes. 247.

2. Color forms can be made from one form in electrotyping. 250.

3. "Flong" is another name for stereotype matrix. 252.

4. Stereotyping may be done either on wet or dry matrices. 252.

5. Stereotypes are cast in shell form, or type high. 252.

6. Wax engraving is the usual method used in the making of maps. 254.

7. Stereotypes will stand up for as many impressions as an electrotype. Fig. 177.

8. Electrotypes may be made more quickly than stereotypes. 252.

9. Corrections can be made in electrotype plates. 250.

10. Electrotypes are: 248.
    1. Photographic reproductions of original drawings.
    2. Copper-faced duplicates of forms or engravings.
    3. Plates cast from a matrix of paper.
    4. Line etchings on zinc.
    5. Brass halftones.

11. Stereotypes are: 252.
    (See answers listed under question 10.)

12. "Sweating on" is a process used to: 251.
    1. Dry ink quickly.
    2. Eliminate offset.
    3. Fasten a binding on a book.
    4. Fasten a plate to a metal base.
    5. Fasten a plate to a wood base.

Chapter XVI

1. Printing ink has the same consistency as thick paint. 255.

2. The same type of ink is used on offset, letterpress, and intaglio presses. 255.

3. Inks, printed in each process, must be suited to the paper stock used to give best results. Fig. 178.

4. Printing ink is made from what two ingredients?   256.

5. Black ink is made from what substance?   257.

6. It is possible to print from watercolor inks on printing presses. 259.

7. Ink used in process color printing is: 264:
    1. Opaque.
    2. Transparent.
    3. Comparable to writing ink.
    4. Soluble in water.
    5. Capable of being mixed in water.

8. What can be put in ink to make it dry quickly by penetration? 265a.
    1. Linseed oil.   4. Varnish.
    2. Japan dryer.   5. Alcohol.
    3. Paste dryer.

9. What happens to ink when it is reduced?   265a.
    1. Made more tacky.
    2. Softened and made less tacky.
    3. Made harder.
    4. Made to dry quickly.
    5. Made to dry by oxidation.

10. What can be put in ink to make it dry more slowly by oxidation?   265a.
    1. Linseed oil.   4. Varnish.
    2. Japan dryer.   5. Alcohol.
    3. Paste dryer.

11. What kind of ink should be used on coated paper?   Fig. 178.
    1. News.   4. Bond.
    2. Halftone.   5. Opaque colored.
    3. Job.

12. What kind of ink should be used on antique paper?   Fig. 178. (See list of answers under question 11.)

13. What kind of ink should be used on bond paper?   Fig. 178.
(See list of answers under question 11.)

14. A color which cannot be made by a mixture of other colors is:
260.
    1. Citrine.   4. Olive.
    2. Blue.   5. Amber.
    3. Russet.

15. A color which cannot be made by a mixture of other colors is:
Fig. 180.
    1. Brown.   4. Gray.
    2. Olive.   5. Magenta.
    3. Yellow.

16. What is mixed with ink to stiffen it?   265a.
    1. No. 00 varnish.
    2. No. 7 varnish.
    3. No. 1 varnish.
    4. No. 0000 varnish.
    5. No. 2 varnish.

17. Ink used in color-process printing is: 264.
    1. Transparent.   4. Halftone ink.
    2. Opaque.   5. Watercolor ink.
    3. Bond ink.

18. Blue and yellow ink mixed in equal quantities make: Fig. 180.
    1. Purple.   4. Green.
    2. Brown.   5. Citrine.
    3. Orange.

19. Red and blue ink mixed in equal quantities make: Fig. 180.
(See list of answers under question 18.)

20. Red and yellow ink mixed in equal quantities make: Fig. 180.
(See list of answers under question 18.)

21. A color which cannot be made by a mixture of other colors is:
Fig. 180.

    1. Russet.   4. Citrine.
    2. Red.   5. Amber.
    3. Olive.

Chapter XVII

1. Copperplate engraving is unequalled in its dense black or color. 266.

2. Copperplate making is done by hand and also by machine. 267.

3. Thermography is a process of printing, dusting the sheets, and then heating to fuse the powder, thus raising the print to appear like engraving.   269.

4. The female die in the embossing process is etched in a plate. 270.

5. Cut outs can be done with steel rule on printing presses.   271.

6. Blind embossing is done while printing.   270.

Chapter XVIII

1. Lithography is the process of: 272.
    1. Printing from a flat stone or plate.
    2. Printing from a glass plate, covered with a gelatin coating.
    3. Printing from an etched copper cylinder.
    4. Printing from a flat zinc plate wrapped about a cylinder.

2. Rotogravure is a process of: 277.
(See list of answers in question 1.)

3. Offset lithography is a process of: **275.**
(See list of answers in question 1.)

4. Zinc offset plates may be regrained for use again.   274.

5. Halftone screens are possible in gravure, lithography, and collotype.   274, 277, 278.

6. Photo-Composing Machines are used for all types of gravure and lithographic presses.   276.

7. Printing from Collotype plates is just as fast as rotogravure. 278, 277.

8. Illustrations in printed matter can be printed faster by lithography than by letterpress.   278a.

9. Collotype is the nearest approach to photographs than is any other known printing process.   278.

10. Press makeready is easier on lithographic presses than on letter press machines.   278a.

11. Type matter can be as clearly produced in lithography as in letterpress.   278a.

CHAPTER XIX

1. Most paper is made from wood pulp.   280.

2. The Fourdrinier brothers invented the papermaking machine about 1804.   279.

3. The first paper was made in England.   279.

4. Calendar rolls put the finish on paper on modern machines. 280.

5. A water mark is: 281.
    1. A feathered edge on a sheet of paper.
    2. A design or lettering pressed into the paper.
    3. Seen on newsprint paper.
    4. Seen on cardboard.
    5. Stamped onto the paper after it is made.

6. A deckle is: 282.
   (See answers listed under question 5.)

7. English finish paper is generally used in printing: 283.
   1. Books.
   2. Daily papers.
   3. Post cards.
   4. Covers.
   5. Stationery.

8. The basis of count and weight in printing papers today is: 284.
   1. The ream.
   2. 500 sheets.
   3. 2000 sheets.
   4. 1000 sheets.
   5. 750 sheets.

9. What basis of weight is 35×38—100 (M): 284.
   1. 50 lbs.
   2. 100 lbs.
   3. 1000 lbs.
   4. 500 lbs.
   5. 25 lbs.

10. What basis of weight is 17×22—40 (M): 284.
    1. 20 lbs.
    2. 17 lbs.
    3. 22 lbs.
    4. 80 lbs.
    5. 44 lbs.

11. One size of bond paper is: 283.
    1. 25×38.
    2. 17×22.
    3. 20×26.
    4. 23×35.
    5. $22\frac{1}{2} \times 28\frac{1}{2}$.

12. One size of book paper is: 283.
    (Use answers listed under question 11.)

13. The two most practical sizes of cover papers are: 283.
    1. 25×38.
    2. 17×22.
    3. 20×26.
    4. 22×35.
    5. 22×34.

14. One size of bristol board is: 283.
    1. 25×38.
    2. 17×22.
    3. 20×26.
    4. $22\frac{1}{2} \times 28\frac{1}{2}$.
    5. 19×28.

15. How many pieces $5\frac{1}{2}\times8\frac{1}{2}$ can be cut from a sheet 17×22? 287.
    1. 6   4. 4.
    2. 7.   5. 10.
    3. 8.

16. How many pieces 3×5 can be cut from a sheet $25\frac{1}{2}\times30\frac{1}{2}$? 287.
    1. 52.   4. 48.
    2. 46.   5. 50.
    3. 42.

17. How many pieces 5×9 can be cut from a sheet $22\frac{1}{2}\times28\frac{1}{2}$? 287.
    1. 10.   4. 8.
    2. 12.   5. 6.
    3. 14.

18. How many pieces 8×12 can be cut from a sheet 32×44? 287.
    1. 10.   4. 16.
    2. 12.   5. 8.
    3. 14.

19. Newsprint is generally used in printing: 283.
    1. Books.   4. Stationery.
    2. Daily papers.   5. Post cards.
    3. Covers.

20. A sheet 25×38—140 (M) is the same basis weight as one 32×44—104 (M). 288.

21. Paper tears with the grain better than against the grain. 289.

22. Paper shrinks and stretches with changes in the relative humidity of a room. 290.

23. How much will 700 sheets 25×38—140 (M) cost at $9\frac{1}{2}$ cents per pound? 288.

24. How much will 253 sheets 17×22—40 (M) cost at 16 cents per pound? 288.

Chapter XX

1. Printers, as a group, are fairly healthy.　291.

2. Men should work alone when cutting paper stock.　291.

3. Guards are not needed on a platen printing press.　291.

4. Men working about machines should not wear long ties and flapping sleeves.　291.

5. Open type cases do not constitute an accident hazard in the composing room.　291.

6. Horseplay is not a hazard in any shop.　291.

7. Holding type in the mouth is permissible in printing plants. 291.

8. Tuberculosis and lead poisoning are "printers' diseases."　291.

9. Skin infections can be caught from unclean wiping cloths.　291.

10. Dry sweeping is a health hazard in composing rooms.　291.

GLOSSARY

ADMAN—A compositor who sets advertisements.

AGATE—5½-point body type.

ALIVE—Type after it has been set, before it is ready for distribution.

ALLEY—Floor space between two type cabinets.

ALUMINOTYPE—A plate made from an aluminum alloy.

ANTIMONY—One of the ingredients of type metal.

ANTIQUE—A rough surfaced paper.

ANTIQUE ROMAN—A style of type.

APPRENTICE—A learner of a trade.

ARABIC NUMERALS—1234567890.

AUTOPRESS—A high-speed cylinder press.

BACKING-UP—Printing the other side of a sheet.

BALANCE—A pleasing arrangement of type masses.

BANK—A stand to hold type and spacing materials.

BASIS WEIGHT—The name given to a sheet of paper in terms of the weight of a ream in a certain size.

BEARD—The beveled space below the face of a type.

BEARERS—Type-high ledges on a press to insure the rollers turning; strips of wood or metal placed inside the ends of platen press chases.

BED—The part of a press on which the form is placed.

BEN DAY PROCESS—A mechanical method of producing a shaded effect on a line plate.

BEVELED RULE—Rule on which the printing surface is on one side.

BILL OF FARE—A menu.

BINDER—A temporary cover. One who does bindery work.

BINDERY—A place where books are assembled.

BLACK-LETTER—A style of type, text or Gothic.

BLANK CASE—A type case minus the partitions.

BLOCK—A hard wood or metal base for plates. A woodcut.

BLOCK LETTER—Gothic or sans-serif.

BODONI—A type family.

BODY—The size of type from the bottom to the top of the letter.

BODY TYPE—Type used for straight composition.

BOND—A strong and translucent rag or sulphite paper.

BOOK PAPER—A class of paper used for making books.

BORDERS—Characters cast in type or in strips used for panels, etc.

BRACES—Characters used to group type matter (——).

BRACKET—Characters used to enclose words, figures, etc., from the text [ ].

BRASSES—Brass leads used in newspaper make-up.

BRASS RULE—Strips of brass to print lines.

BRASS SPACES—Spaces 1-point thick.

BRAYER—An ink roller used for proofing.

BRILLIANT—A small size of type, now 4-point.

BRISTOL BOARD—A fine grade of cardboard.

BROADSIDE—A specially folded advertising sheet.

BROCHURE—A small booklet.

BRONZE POWDER—A fine powder to give brilliant glossy effects in gold, silver, etc.

BRONZING—Brushing a fine bronze powder over a freshly printed sheet, which adheres to the print.

BUNDLING MACHINE—A machine used for compressing signatures, padding, etc.

BUTTED—Slugs placed end to end to form one line.

CABINET—An enclosed chest to hold type cases.

CALENDER—A paper-making machine device which gives the high gloss to papers.

CALIFORNIA JOB CASE—A type storage case.

CANON—An old size of type, now 48 point.

CAP—Capital letters.   A size 14×17 in. sheet of paper.

CAPTION—A heading or title.

CAR CARD—A large card bearing an advertisement, used in cars and busses.

CARDBOARD—A thick, stiff paper.

CASE—A shallow tray divided into compartments, used to hold types.

CASEIN—An albuminous substance used for sizing paper.

CASE STAND—A framework used to hold type cases.

CASLON—An oldstyle roman type, originated by William Caslon.

CAST—To pour metal into a mold.

CAXTON BLACK—A black gothic type face.

CELLULOSE—A fibrous substance used to make paper, obtained from cotton, linen, hemp and wood.

CENTERED—Placed in the center of a sheet, or line.

CENTURY—A type face.

CHALK OVERLAY—An overlay mechanically made in making ready type forms and plate forms on the press.

CHALK-PLATE ENGRAVING—A process of making illustrations by engraving the design on a chalk-covered plate, and casting as in stereotyping.

CHAPEL—An organization of workmen in a printing office.

CHASE—An iron or steel frame in which type forms are locked for the press.

CHELTENHAM—A name of a family of type faces.

CHROMA—The degree of intensity from black to white in color.

CIRCULARS—Advertising matter in the form of letters and handbills.

CLARENDON—A style of type.

CLAY-FINISH PAPER—A paper in which fine clay is used to smoothen the surface.

CLEAN PROOF—A term used when few errors are found on a proof.

CLOISTER—A type face.

CLOSED SHOP—A shop in which only union workmen are employed.

COATED PAPER—A smooth and glossy-finished paper.

COLLATING—Examining the folded signatures of a book in the process of gathering to see that all sections are in order.

COLOPHON—An inscription in a book telling of the printing thereof.

COLOR FILTER—A sheet of colored glass used in photographing for color plates.

COLOR FORM—The form making the second color in a job of printing.

COLT'S ARMORY PRESS—A platen press built on the Universal pattern.

COLUMN—A vertical series of lines side by side, as in newspaper composition.

COLUMN RULES—Strips of rule, printing equipment used between columns in newspaper composition.

COMBINATION HALFTONE—A printing plate made up of the half-tone and line-etching processes.

COMPOSING MACHINES—Machines producing single types and regular composition mechanically.

COMPOSITION—Typesetting and arranging types.

COMPOSITOR—One who sets type.

CONDENSED—Thin type faces.

COPPERPLATE ENGRAVING—The practice of making impressions from intaglio plates.

COPPERPLATE GOTHIC—A series of type faces made in the sans-serif style.

COPPER SPACES—Spaces $\frac{1}{2}$-point thick.

COPY—That which the printer copies in his work.

COPY-CUTTER—One who divides copy into pieces of small size which are given to compositors in newspaper shops.

COPYHOLDER—One who holds copy and reads aloud therefrom to the proofreader.

COPYREADER—Same as copyholder.

COVER PAPERS—Heavy, decorative papers used for covering pamphlets, etc.

CREASING—Bending sheets of paper to make them lie flat.

CROP—To cut down printing plates.

CUT—An engraving or an electrotype or stereotype.

CUT CARDS—Cardboard cut to standard sizes.

Cut-Off Rule—A rule used to separate advertisements in newspaper make-up.

Cutting Rule—Steel rule used to cut out designs on a printing press.

Cylinder Press—Style of printing machine which prints by the action of a cylinder on a flat form.

Dandy Roller—A wire cylinder on a paper-making machine that makes the wove or laid effect of the paper; also the watermark.

Dashes—Straight lines in en and em widths cast in sizes from 5 to 24 point.

Dead—Type ready for distribution.

Dead-Line—Last day or hour in which copy is acceptable.

Deckle Edge—An untrimmed feather edge.

Devil—The youngest apprentice in a printing office.

Diamond—$4\frac{1}{2}$-point type.

Die Stamping—Intaglio printing done by means of a die and counter die.

Diphthong—Two vowels joined together, as æ, œ, etc.

Dirty Proof—A proof containing many errors.

Disc Ruling Machine—A machine for ruling lines with discs rather than steel pens.

Disc—The flat circular plate on a platen press upon which the ink is distributed.

Display—Composition in which various sizes of types are used.

Display Type—The largest and heavier faces of type.

Distribution—The placing of type and spacing material back into the cases.

Drier—A substance added to ink to assist in drying.

Drum Cylinder Press—A printing machine with an extra large cylinder, which carries the paper to the impression.

Dull-Finish Paper—Coated stock with glossy finish removed.

Dummy—Pages of a planned book put together to assist in determining the specifications, etc.; the "layout" of a book or pamphlet.

Dump—The place where dead matter is stored.

DUPLEX PRESS—A printing machine which prints both sides of the paper in one passage through the press.

ELECTROTYPE—A duplicate of a type form or plate.

ELZEVIR OLDSTYLE—A style of type face.

EM—The square of the type body of any size; the unit for measuring printing material by 12-point ems.

EMBOSSING—Impressing letters and figures in relief.

EN—One-half the width of the em.

ENAMELED PAPER—Paper coated with clay, glue and other substances, having a glossy finish.

ENGRAVING—The process of cutting letters and designs into a plate for the purpose of making impressions.

ENVELOPE CORNER CARD—The printed address in the upper left-hand corner of envelopes.

ESPARTO—A paper-making fiber made from a grass.

ETCHING—A method of making printing plates by the action of acid on the plate.

EXPANDED—A very thick type face.

EXTRA CONDENSED—A very thin type face.

FACE—The part of the type that makes the impression.

FAMILY—A group of related type faces in series.

FAN OUT—To separate sheets by gently rubbing them to form a fan-shaped pile.

FARM OUT—To sublet a job of printing.

FEEDER—A person who hand-feeds a press. An automatic press sheet feeder.

FEED GUIDES—Appliances used for holding sheets in position while printing.

FEET—The two lower projections of a piece of type.

FENDER—A strip of cardboard used to hold sheets on a press.

FLAT BED—Said of a press printing from a flat form or plate.

FLONG—A matrix used in stereotyping.

FLUSH—To the end of either side, or end of a line, as "set flush right" in type composition.

FOLD—Doubling over a sheet of paper.

FOLIO—A sheet folded once, consisting of two leaves forming four pages.

FONT—An assortment of any one size and style of type.

FORWARDING—The process of binding a book after the sheets are fastened together.

FOURDRINIER—A paper-making machine.

FURNITURE—Pieces of wood and metal to fill large blank spaces in printing forms.

GALLEY—A shallow tray in which type is placed for assembling or storage.

GALLEY PRESS—A proofing machine.

GARAMOND—A style of type face.

GATHERING—Collecting signatures of a book.

GAUGE—A piece of metal used to hold sheets in a press in the correct position for printing.

GOLDING JOBBER—A platen press.

GORDON PRESS—A style of platen press.

GOSS PRESS—A perfecting printing press.

GRAIN—The direction in which the fibers lie in a sheet of paper.

GRIPPERS—Iron fingers on a platen press to hold the sheets to the platen.

GUDGEONS—Metal wheels used on press roller stocks.

GUIDE—Feed gauges against which the sheets are fed in the printing presses.

GUTTER—The back margin of a book sheet.

HAIRLINE—The fine and delicate lines in a type or engraving.

HAIR SPACES—Very thin spaces used in typesetting.

HALF-DIAMOND INDENTION—When successive lines are indented each slightly more than the other in straight composition.

HALF TITLE—The title placed at the head of the first chapter of a book.

HALFTONE—A printing plate made by the photographic and chemical processes, in which the picture is made up of a series of very small dots.

HANDBILL—A small printed advertisement.

HARMONY—The state of a pleasing relation between parts of a piece of printing.

HARRIS PRESS—An offset printing machine.

HEAD—The top of a book; the title of a newspaper article.

HELL BOX—A receptacle in which broken type is placed.

HIGH LIGHTS—The lightest parts of a printing plate.

HOE PRESS—The trade name for divers cylinder presses.

HOT EMBOSSING—The process of embossing with the use of heated dies.

HYPOTENUSE OBLONG—A page proportion in which the depth is 50 per cent more than its width.

IMITATION EMBOSSING—Thermography.

IMPOSING TABLE—The flat stone- or metal-topped table on which forms are locked for the press.

IMPOSITION—The proper placing of page forms in a chase.

IMPRESSION—The pressure of type forms or plates on a piece of paper.

IMPRESSION SCREWS—The adjusting screws that regulate the position of the platen on a platen press.

INDENT—To space before a line in type composition.

INFERIOR FIGURES OR LETTERS—Small figures or letters cast on the lower part of a type, thus: 1 2 3 or a b c.

INITIAL LETTER—The larger letter beginning a piece of straight composition.

INK FOUNTAIN—A device to feed small quantities of ink to printing rollers on a press.

INSERT—An extra sheet placed in a book.

INTAGLIO—Engraving cut into either wood or metal.

INTERTYPE—A slug-casting composing machine, similar to the Linotype.

ITALIC—Slanting types.

JENSON—A type face; also the name of a famous Venetian printer.

JOBBER—A press for small work.

Job Compositor—A typesetter who sets commercial work.

Job Font—A small assortment of type in any one size and style.

Job Galley—A small tray used in job composition.

Job Printer—A printer doing small commercial printing.

Job Ticket—Usually an envelope containing copy, on which directions concerning the job are given.

Job Type—Type faces used in printing small commercial work.

Jog—To straighten sheets of paper.

Journeyman—A printer who has finished his apprenticeship.

Kelly Press—An automatically fed cylinder printing machine.

Kennerley—A style of type face.

Kern—The part of the face of a type that extends over the body.

Key—A device used in operating quoins.

Key Plate—The plate used as a guide to register other plates in color printing.

Kidder Press—A style of printing press, usually rotary machines.

Knee—The movable piece on a composing stick.

Klymax Feeder—A style of sheet feeder attachable to a platen press.

Kraft Paper—A tough wrapping paper.

Labor Saving—Any printing material cut to small, assorted lengths.

Laid Paper—Paper having parallel lines watermarked at equal distances apart.

Laureate Press—A platen press with a perpendicular, rigid bed.

Lay of the Case—The arrangement of the letters in a type case.

Layout—The plan of a job of printing.

Layout Paper—Paper used in laying out, having pica squares ruled upon it as guides.

Lead Cutter—A device to cut leads to small sizes.

Leaders—Periods or dots at intervals to lead the eye in tabular matter, etc.

Leads—Thin strips of metal used to space between lines of type.

Letterhead—A printed heading on letter paper.

LETTERPRESS—Printing from raised letters, as from type.

LETTER SPACING—Spacing between letters in type composition.

LIBERTY PRESS—A style of platen press.

LIFT—When a form, after being locked up, and each piece of type is held securely, it is said to "lift."

LIGATURE—Two or more letters tied together and cast in one piece of type, as fi, ff, fl, ffi, ffl.

LIGHT FACE—A term used for a face of type of lighter form than usual.

LINE CUT—See line engraving.

LINE ENGRAVING—A printing plate made up of black and white; a zinc etching.

LINE GAUGE.—See Pica rule.

LINEN FINISH—A paper or cardboard having a finish similar to that of linen cloth.

LINING—The aligning of type faces at the bottom of the letters.

LINOGRAPH—A machine that casts slug lines, similar to the Linotype and Intertype.

LINOTYPE—A slug-casting machine.

LITHOGRAPHY—The process of printing from a stone or plate.

LIVE—A printing form still in use.

LOGOTYPE—Several letters or a whole word cast on one body, as *The, and,* etc.

LONG PRIMER—An old name for 10 point.

LOWERCASE—Small letters.

LUDLOW TYPOGRAPH—A slug-casting machine in which the matrices are set by hand.

MACHINE COMPOSITION—Any type composition done mechanically.

MACHINE FINISH—A smooth paper used in printing books.

MAKEREADY—Preparing a press to print from the form in the best way.

MAKING UP—Arranging types and materials into a form.

MAKE-UP RULE—A flat piece of steel helpful in making up.

MARGIN—The space between the edge of the paper and the print.

Matrix—A mold in which a type is cast; the paper mold used in stereotyping.

Miehle Press—A flat-bed two-revolution cylinder press.

Miehle Vertical—A cylinder press in which the form stands vertically.

Miller Feeder—A feeding attachment made for use on platen presses.

Misprint—A typographical error.

Modern Roman—A style of type face.

Mold—The part of a typecasting machine in which the type or line is cast.

Monotype—A composing machine which casts individual types similar to foundry type.

Mortise—The cut-out portion of an electro or engraving in which type is set.

Multicolor Press—A press in which all colors are printed in one time through the machine.

Mutton Quad—An em quad.

Neck—The part of a type between the shoulder and the face.

News Cases—A pair of type cases in which the capitals are kept in the upper case, and the small letters are kept in the lower case.

Newsprint—A paper made from wood pulp.

News Stick—A composing stick with a fixed measure.

New York Job Case—A type case with boxes for capitals, lower-case, and small capitals.

Nick—A notch in a type which acts as a guide for the typesetter.

Nonpareil—The equivalent of 6 points; a size of type now called 6 point.

Numbering Machine—A type-high printing machine which is locked in regular type forms, and prints numbers in consecutive order.

Nut Quad—An en quad.

Offset Printing—A lithographic process in which the plate prints on a rubber cylinder, which in turn offsets the print to the paper.

OLD ENGLISH—A style of black-faced text type.

OLDSTYLE—A type style with diagonally sloping serifs.

ONIONSKIN—A thin paper.

OPEN MATTER—Type lines very widely spaced.

OPTICAL CENTER—The center of a rectangle as it appears to the eye; two-fifths from the top of the rectangle.

OPTIMUS PRESS—A style of two-revolution cylinder press.

OUTLINE HALFTONE—A halftone plate in which the background is cut away.

OVERLAY—In press makeready, a piece of paper placed in the tympan to make part of the form print heavier in that place.

OVERRUNNING—Setting type backward or forward in making corrections.

PACKAGE LABEL—A gummed slip of paper, for sticking addresses on packages.

PAD—A number of sheets of paper stuck together by gluing one side of the pile.

PAMPHLET—Several sheets of paper stitched together.

PANEL—A square or rectangular design made up of rule or border.

PEARL—An old size of type, now 5 point.

PEBBLING—A process of graining, crimping, etc., paper to relieve the eye of shiny effects.

PEERLESS PRESS—An old style of platen press.

PERFECTING—Printing on both sides of the paper.

PERFORATING MACHINE—A machine used to perforate small holes in a row to facilitate tearing.

PHOTO-ENGRAVING—The process of making printing plates by the action of light on a film.

PHOTOGRAVURE—The process of printing from an intaglio engraving.

PHOTOLITHOGRAPHY—The process of placing a design on a lithographic plate or stone by photography.

PI—Mixed type.

PICA—The standard unit of measurement for printing material. Twelve-point type.

PIGMENT—Substance used for coloring in printing ink.

PIN MARK—The mark made by a pin that ejects a type from the mold in casting.

PLANER—A smooth block used to knock type to its feet.

PLATE—A duplicate of type forms. A piece of engraved metal used in printing illustrations.

PLATE CYLINDER—The cylinder on a rotary press holding the printing form.

PLATEN—The flat part of a platen press facing the bed, on which the tympan is placed.

PLATEN PRESS—A style of press that makes impressions from a flat surface.

POINT—A mark of punctuation; also, the unit of measurement of printing material.

POINT-SET—Letters of a type font which are cast to point multiples.

POINT SYSTEM—The measurement of all printing material is made on the point system.

POSITIVE—Corresponding with the original in making printing plates.

POTTER PRESS—A style of offset press; also a make of proof press.

PREMIER PRESS—A style of two-revolution cylinder press.

PRESS—A machine for making printed impressions.

PRESS FEEDERS—Those who hand-feed a printing press; also applied to automatic feeding devices placed on printing presses.

PRESSMAN—One who makes ready on presses.

PRESS PROOFS—Proofs made on the regular printing presses.

PRIMARY COLORS—Yellow, red and blue.

PRINTING INK—A pasty substance used to print from types and plates on paper.

PRINTER'S MARKS—Emblems or trade-marks of printers.

PROCESS ENGRAVING—See Thermography; also Engraving.

PROCESS PRINTING—Printing from color plates with process inks and plates.

PROGRESSIVE PROOFS—Proofs of color plates used as a guide to the pressman.

PROOF—The first print of a printing form, read to detect possible errors.

PROOF PLANER—A felt-bottomed block used to take proofs by hand.

PROOF PRESS—A machine for making prints of forms and plates.

PROOFREADER—One who reads proofs and marks errors for correction.

PROOFREADER'S MARKS—Signs used by proofreaders to denote errors.

PROOF ROLLER—A small hand-inking roller; a brayer.

PROPORTION—Comparative relationship between the elements of a piece of printing.

PULL A PROOF—To make a print for proofreading.

PULP—The mass of material used to make sheets of paper.

PUNCH—The original die used in typefounding.

PUNCHING MACHINE—A contrivance used to punch holes in paper.

QUADS—Blank types used to space out at the ends of lines in type composition.

QUOIN KEY—A tool used to manipulate quoins.

QUOINS—Small wedges used in locking up type forms for the press.

QUOTATION FURNITURE—Small sizes of metal furniture.

RACK—A framework used to hold type storage cases.

RAILROAD FURNITURE—Metal furniture similar to the shape of railroad rails.

RAISED PRINTING—See Thermography.

READY PRINT—Inside sections of newspapers bought printed with feature articles, comics, etc.

REAM—Five hundred sheets of paper constitute a "printer's ream."

REGISTER—The adjustment of pages so that they will print in the correct position over another printed form.

REGLET—Wooden pieces similar to 6- and 12-point slugs.

RELIEF PRINTING—Letterpress printing.

REVERSE PLATE—A printing plate in which the black and white has been reversed.

REVISE—A second proof taken to check on errors.

ROLLERS—Printing rollers.

ROLL-LEAF STAMPING—A process of stamping gold leaf on covers of books and like work.

ROMAN NUMERALS—The Roman system of notation, in which the following symbols are used: I = 1; V = 5; X = 10; L = 50; C = 100; D = 500; M = 1,000.

ROMAN TYPE—The regular style of type used in book and newspaper composition.

ROTOGRAVURE—The process of making intaglio impressions on a rotary press.

ROUGHING—See Pebbling.

ROUTER—A device used to cut away surplus metal from printing plates.

RUBRICATOR—One who ornamented initial letters and other parts of ancient manuscripts and printed books.

RULE—Strips of brass or lead used to print straight lines.

RULE CUTTER—A device for cutting rule to size.

RULING MACHINE—A machine used to pen-rule lines on papers, as on billheads and statements.

RUNNING HEAD—The title of a book printed at the head of each page.

RUNNING TITLE—See Running Head.

RUN IN—Proofreaders mark the proof "run in" when they do not wish the matter to be paragraphed.

RUN OUT—To make a hanging indention.

SADDLE STITCH—To fasten a pamphlet by stitching it through the middle fold of the sheets.

SAFETY PAPER—Paper treated by usually printing in a light tint a design, which assures against forgery.

S. AND C.—Sized and calendered paper; smooth-finished paper.

S. AND S. C.—Sized and supercalendered, a glossy paper.

SANS-SERIF—American gothic type faces; type having no serifs.

SAW TRIMMER—A machine designed to cut linotype slugs and other material to point size.

SCALE—A list of wages or prices.

SCARE HEAD—A very large newspaper heading.

SCORE—To crease paper to facilitate folding.

SCOTCH ROMAN—A style of type face.

SCREW CHASE—A chase used in newspaper offices with screws on the top and side to tighten the form.

SCRIBE—One who copied books by hand before the invention of printing.

SCRIPT TYPE—A style of type similar to handwriting.

SECONDS—Inferior material.

SECTION—A signature, or group of signatures.

SERIF—The short cross-line at the ends of the main strokes of some styles of type faces.

SETTING A STICK—Adjusting a composing stick to measure.

SHEETWISE—Pages imposed in two forms.

SHORT AND—The mark &; ampersand.

SHOULDER—The part of a type not covered by the face.

SHOW CARD—A large advertising placard.

SIDE HEAD—A heading set to the side of the main composition.

SIDE STITCH—The fastening of pamphlet sheets together sideways.

SIGNATURE—A section of a book; the letter or figure appearing at the bottom of the first page of a signature to guide the binder.

SIGNATURE MARK—A printed guide to the binder printed in the gutter of a signature.

SIGNATURE PRESS—A machine used to press together signatures in a bindery to make the books flat.   See Smashing.

SIZE—A sticky yellowish ink used in bronzing.

SKELETON—The border and blank space of a printing form before placing in the type matter.

SKELETON CHASE—A large iron frame, with dovetail slots in which crossbars fit.

SLITTER—A device used to cut or slit paper as it passes through a press.

SLUG—A thick lead, 6 points and upward; a line cast on a type-setting machine.

SLUG-CASTING MACHINES—See Linotype, Ludlow.

SMALL CAPS—Capital letters of smaller size than the usual capital letters provided with a font of type.

SMASHING—Pressing signatures together so that they will lay flat.

SOLID MATTER—Type composition not leaded.

SORTS—The types in a box in a type case.

SPACE—Metal blank used in spacing between words in type composition.

SQUARE FOUR—Four pages imposed so that when printed on both sides, and cut, two sections of four pages each are made.

STANDING MATTER—Type composition held over for another printing.

STAMPING PRESS—A machine used in embossing.

STEAM TABLE—Equipment used in drying matrices in stereotyping.

STEEL ENGRAVING—See Copperlate Engraving.

STEREOTYPE—A printing plate cast from a paper matrix.

STIPPLE—A printing surface on printing plates that consists of fine dots.

STOCK—Paper.

STONE MAN—A workman who locks up forms and imposes pages in a printing plant.

STOP CYLINDER PRESS—A cylinder press in which the cylinder stops between impressions.

STRAIGHT MATTER—Plain composition, as in this printing.

SUB—An abbreviation for substitute, used in print-shop chapels.

SUBHEAD—A secondary title or heading.

SUPERCALENDERED—Extra smooth paper stock.

SUPERIOR FIGURES OR LETTERS—Small letters or figures cast on the extreme upper part of the body, for reference purposes; thus: [123, abc].

SWEATING ON—A process of fastening a printing plate on a metal base.

SYMMETRY—The arrangement of elements over a given axis, so that a division through that axis will divide it into halves.

TABLETS—Sheets of paper glued together at one end.

TABULAR MATTER—Lists of matter in columns, usually separated by blank space or lines.

TACK—Stickiness, as in printing ink.

TEXT—Straight or body matter of a book.

TEXT TYPE—Usually black letter patterned after the old script of hand-written books.

THERMOGRAPHY—The process of dusting freshly printed sheets with powder, so that when heated the powder fuses, forming a raised surface of the print.

THICK SPACE—The 3 em space.

THROW-OFF LEVER—A device for keeping a platen press from making an impression while the press is running.

TINT—A very light color.

TINT BLOCK—A block for printing a very light color.

TISSUE—A very thin paper used in make ready.

TRANSPOSE—To change a word or letter from one place to another.

TRIPLE CASE—A type storage drawer for holding three fonts of type.

TWEEZERS—Small nippers used in handling small sizes of type.

TWO-LINE LETTER—An initial letter covering two lines of the text matter.

TWO-REVOLUTION PRESS—A cylinder press that makes two revolutions of the cylinder in printing one sheet of paper.

TWO-THIRDER—An advanced apprentice who has served two-thirds of his apprenticeship.

TYING UP—The process of wrapping type forms with cord to keep them from being pied.

TYMPAN—The paper that covers the platen or cylinder on a press.

TYPARY COMPOSING MACHINE—A photographic composing machine used in lithographic printing.

TYPE—Printers' letters, made of metal, having a character cast in relief on one end.

TYPEFOUNDING—The making of types.

TYPE HIGH—The standard height of type, .918 of an inch.

TYPOTABULAR SYSTEM—An assortment of small 6-point squares, which may be divided by brass rule, used in setting tabular matter.

TYPOGRAPHER—A master printer.

TYPOGRAPHY—The art of printing from movable types.

TYPOGRAPHICAL UNION—An organization of compositors.

UNDERSCORE—To set a rule under a word or sentence in type composition.

UNDERLAY—A piece of paper placed under a form in making ready.

UNIT—A standard of measurement.

UNIVERSAL PRESS—A style of platen press.

VANDERCOOK PRESS—A style of proof press.

VARNISH—A substance used in making printing ink, the vehicle.

VIGNETTE—Halftone plates in which the background gradually fades away.

VIRKOTYPE—A thermograph machine.

WASHINGTON PRESS—A style of hand press, now obsolete.

WATERMARK—A faint design or lettering pressed into paper while it is still in pulp form.

WAX ENGRAVING—The process of making printing plates by engraving in wax, then electrotyping.

WAYZGOOSE—An old-time printers' festival.

WEB PRESS—A printing machine in which the paper is fed from a roll.

WEIGHT FONT—Type bought by the weight, to fill a standard-size type case.

WHITE SPACE—That part of a piece of printing not covered with type matter.

WICKERSHAM QUOIN—A one-piece locking device used in locking type in a chase.

WIRE STITCHER—A machine for fastening books and pamphlets together.

WOODCUT—A wood engraving; an illustration engraved on wood.

WORK-AND-TURN—Imposing all pages of a section of a book on one form, then turning for a second printing on the other side.

Wove Paper—Paper having the appearance of a piece of cloth, having fine lines running each way of the sheet.

Wrong Font—A wrong face of type in a piece of composition.

Yankee Job Case—A style of type storage drawer.

Zinc Etching—A printing plate made by photography and the chemical processes of acid.

Zinc Halftone—A cheaper form of halftone made in a coarse screen on zinc.

INDEX

Numbers refer to pages, not to sections.

318 · INDEX